DONNA VITEK

Blue Mist of Morning

Published by Silhouette Books New York

America's Publisher of Contemporary Romance

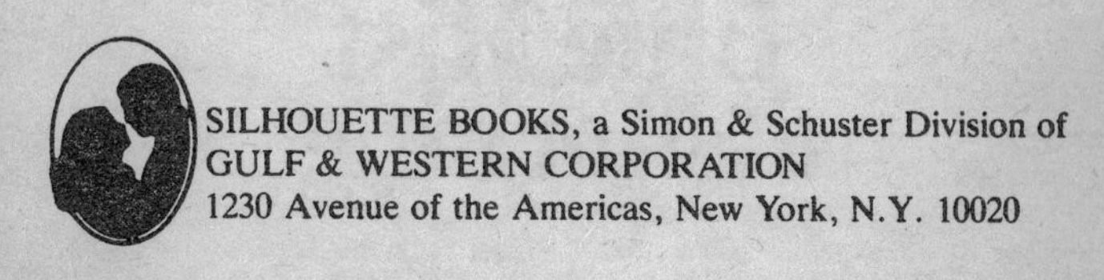

SILHOUETTE BOOKS, a Simon & Schuster Division of
GULF & WESTERN CORPORATION
1230 Avenue of the Americas, New York, N.Y. 10020

Distributed by Pocket Books

ISBN: 0-671-57217-2

First Silhouette Books printing April, 1983

10 9 8 7 6 5 4 3 2 1

Map by Ray Lundgren

America's Publisher of Contemporary Romance

Printed in the U.S.A.

Other Silhouette Books by Donna Vitek

A Different Dream
Showers of Sunlight
Promises from the Past
Veil of Gold
Where the Heart Is
Valaquez Bride
Garden of the Moongate
Game of Chance
Sweet Surrender

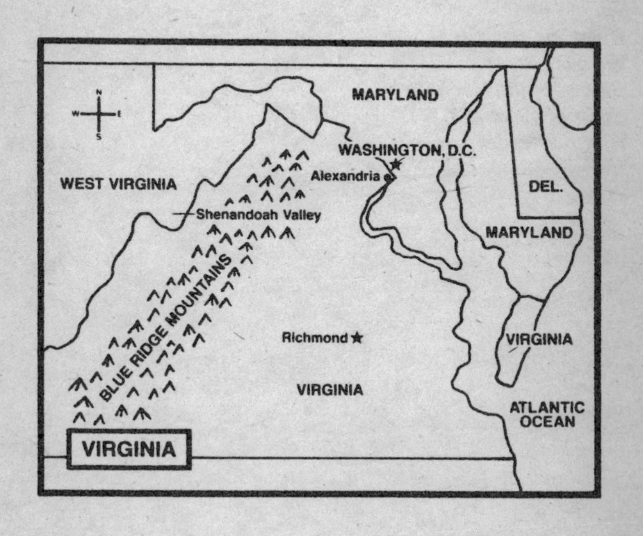
N
W
E
S
MARYLAND
WASHINGTON, D.C.
Alexandria
WEST VIRGINIA
DEL.
Shenandoah Valley
MARYLAND
BLUE RIDGE MOUNTAINS
Richmond
VIRGINIA
VIRGINIA
ATLANTIC
OCEAN
VIRGINIA

Chapter One

The narrow ribbon of road wound over the crest of Virginia's Blue Ridge Mountains. Below, the green rolling hills of the Shenandoah Valley lay darkly shadowed beneath a gray overcast sky. Through the heart of the valley, its famous silver river threaded a serpentine path of intricate coils and loops. In the summertime, bluegrass meadows and shaded secluded glens enhanced the pastoral beauty, but Anne Fairchild reluctantly ignored the scenic view and instead gazed intently at the road ahead. A late March snowstorm, unexpected and, therefore, unnerving, was making driving difficult. As a chilling wind swirled the fine, thickly falling flakes against the windshield, she slowed her speed, then sensed she was being watched by the man in the seat beside her.

As she glanced warily at her new boss, Ty Manning, her honest gray eyes quickly took in his large, lean yet muscular frame clad in a superbly tailored charcoal gray pin-striped suit. His coat was unbuttoned, as was his vest and, although his wine-colored tie was loosened at the collar and the top button of his white shirt was undone, he still looked sufficiently authoritative. He didn't smile and met her swiftly appraising gaze with steady blue eyes.

"Obviously, the weather service didn't foresee this," he commented matter-of-factly, his voice deep-timbred and pleasantly melodious. "The road is pretty well covered already. Are you getting tired of driving?"

Peering intently out the windshield again, Anne shook her head, then brushed back the strand of thick honey-blond hair that grazed her cheek. "I'm fine," she exaggerated slightly. "I just slowed down a little because it's beginning to get harder to see."

With a perfunctory nod, Mr. Manning shuffled through the papers contained in the open leather briefcase he held on his lap, then began to peruse an intricate contract Anne had typed that morning. "If you do get tired, just speak up," he said, almost as an afterthought. "Mike can drive again."

"Yes, sir," Anne murmured and stole a quick glance back over her shoulder. A slight smile curved her softly shaped lips. Stretched out on the back seat, using her uncrushable down coat as a pillow, Mike Bennett, one of Manning Consultants' lawyers, was peacefully asleep.

Actually, she should have been a bit annoyed at him. After leaving Alexandria at two that afternoon, he had only driven twenty miles or so before pleading weariness and asking her to take the wheel. She had been driving ever since, almost three hours, and although the snow was making the going rough, Mike hadn't once offered to take over for her. Still, she couldn't really be mad at him. On the contrary, she was somewhat relieved that he had come along on this trip. The weekend was going to be spent discussing business with Kirt Callen, one of Manning's clients. Since she had known Mike for two years and had even gone out to dinner with him on a couple of occasions, she felt sure his presence this weekend would make her feel more comfortable. Ty Manning himself was still practically a stranger.

As she followed the snow-covered road's winding descent, she eyed her new boss surreptitiously out of the corner of her eye. He was something of an enigma. Although she had worked for Manning Consultants for four years, she had never really had much contact with Ty Manning. She had begun in the stenographers' pool. As the years passed, other girls had frequently come and gone, but she had stayed with the firm and moved upward through the ranks to the position of executive secretary to the vice-president. Then, two weeks ago, Ty Manning's own secretary, out on maternity leave, had decided to stay home with her newborn child, and Anne had been promoted. At the relatively young age of twenty-three, she found it gratifying to be trusted with the responsible position of secretary to the president of a firm as large and as diversified as Manning Consultants. And the increase in salary had been a godsend. Yet, Anne did wish she had a clearer perception of the person Ty Manning really was. Knowing all the little quirks and eccentricities of one's boss was compulsory for a secretary who wanted to be an unqualified success. But, unfortunately, Anne's two weeks in Mr. Manning's office hadn't provided her with many enlightening insights into his personality.

Outwardly, he was always polite and thoroughly businesslike in his dealings with her. Luckily, she had not displeased him thus far, but she had seen his displeasure directed at others and had been impressed and somewhat intimidated. He was slow to anger, but when his temper did erupt, he could wither a person with a searing stare and chastise without ever raising his voice. A few choice words, spoken in a deep, deceptively soft tone, could reduce most of his employees to jelly. He was the perfect executive: calm, cool, decisive and always in control. So, Anne was striving hard to be the equally perfect, efficient secretary who could eventually anticipate his every action and need, thereby becoming indispensable to him. As for actually being able to relax around him, Anne wasn't sure she ever could. He was rather aloof and conveyed such strength of will that she was fairly certain their working relationship would always remain distant, impersonal and strictly professional.

As she glanced sideways at him again, a tiny frown marred the ivory smoothness of her brow. Sometimes, she found it difficult to believe the rumors she had heard about his personal life. According to the office gossips, he didn't lack for female companionship. Supposedly, some of Alexandria's most prominent young socialites competed for his attention, and Anne herself had seen pictures of him and some of those young women printed on the society page of the local newspaper. Anne realized that she shouldn't be surprised women found him irresistible. The girls at the office certainly swooned over him, whispering constantly about how sexy he was and tittering like adolescents whenever he happened to speak to one of them. He was attractive. There was no denying that fact. He was tall and fit, muscular yet not in the least burly, and there didn't seem to be a surplus ounce of weight on him. He was thirty-five years old, and maturity and strength were evidenced in the angular contours of his lean sun-browned face. There was a rather sensuous curve in his firmly shaped lips and an aura of virile masculinity about him, but Anne was immune to the magnetic sexuality the other girls oohed and aahed about. Ty Manning was her boss, and she never wanted to see him as anything more than the cool, brusque businessman she dealt with every day. At eighteen, in her first job, she had been foolish enough to succumb to the charms of her employer. And that was a mistake she'd resolved never to make again.

Shifting to a more comfortable position in the bucket seat, she watched the road ahead carefully, wincing with each sharp, tortuous curve she had to negotiate. The silence in the car was broken only by the soft swish of the windshield wipers and the occasional rattle of papers in Ty Manning's briefcase. About ten minutes later, Anne cautiously braked to a stop at an intersection. After consulting the roadmap on which Mr. Manning had traced the route to his mountain retreat with a red pencil, she turned onto the steeply ascending road to her left. To make the steep incline, she accelerated more than she should have, and her heart lurched as the road suddenly swooped down into a sloping hairpin curve. She hit the brakes, her second mistake, and suddenly Ty Manning's sleek black Mercedes sedan skidded on a patch of ice beneath the snow that covered the road. Uttering a soft little cry, Anne fought to control the swerving car, but it was useless. Momentum defeated her. Almost as if in slow motion, the Mercedes slid across the road and settled heavily to rest, atilt in a deep side ditch.

Ty Manning's briefcase slid from his lap. Papers scattered over the floorboard, and had it not been for the seat belt he was wearing, he would have probably landed on Anne. As it was, she was mortified. Squeezing her eyes shut, she steeled herself for an explosion of temper.

Oddly enough, it was Mike Bennett who erupted. His nap rudely interrupted, he suddenly found himself sliding along the back seat with Anne's coat, which he had been using as a pillow, covering his face so he couldn't see. He was far from happy. Jerking the coat off his head, he uttered an explicit curse. "How the devil did you manage to land us in a ditch, Anne?" he growled. "I thought you said you could drive. Of all the clumsy, inept . . ."

"That's enough, Mike," Ty Manning interrupted tersely, giving the younger man one of his sternest silencing glares. Then he turned his cold blue eyes on Anne. "Are you all right?"

She gulped, then gave a jerky nod of her head. "I'm just sort of squashed up against the door, but I'm not hurt or anything. Oh, Mr. Manning, I'm so sorry. It all just happened so fast. I'm terribly sorry if I've damaged your car, but, well . . . I . . . usually I'm a good driver, really I am. I've never had an accident before in my life. I'm truly sorry, believe me. I . . ." As he stared at her, the expression in his blue eyes beyond analysis, her voice trailed off. The uneasy silence was broken almost immediately by Mike's thoroughly disgusted sigh.

Ty Manning shot him another withering glance, then said quite calmly, "I think we can blame the weather for this accident, not you, Miss Fairchild. Now, we'd better concern ourselves with getting out of the car." With amazing ease, he thrust open the door on the passenger side, unfastened his seat and shoulder belts, and lithely lifted himself out to drop to his feet on the snowy road with the graceful lightness of a big cat. As Mike struggled to open the back door to make his escape, Ty leaned back into the car, reaching out a lean tan hand.

Unable to look at him, Anne fumbled with the catch of her own seat belt. Her hands were still shaking so much from the shock of the accident that it took her some time to release it. Even when she had freed herself, she hesitated for a few tense seconds before finally, reluctantly, raising her arm. Her small slender hand was enveloped in Ty's much larger one. Strong fingers curved around her delicate wrist, gripping securely yet with astonishing gentleness. Then, almost before she could catch her breath, she was lifted halfway through the open door. In the next moment Ty's hands spanned her waist as he drew her out of the car and lowered her to the ground.

When he released her at once, she hastily smoothed the skirt of the beige wool jersey dress she wore. As he turned away to assess the damage to his car, she valiantly tried to subdue the tendril of hair that habitually escaped the otherwise-neat braided chignon on her nape, but her efforts were in vain, as usual. As if by magic, the strand escaped again to fall forward and tickle one flushed cheek. The cold wind was beginning to permeate her lightweight wool dress, and she rubbed her hands briskly over the long, cuffed sleeves covering her arms. She shifted her feet restlessly, grateful that it had been raining that morning when she had left for work. Lacking rubber rainboots, she had instead worn her knee-high brown leather boots, so at least it didn't matter that she was now standing in about four inches of snow.

Following Ty and Mike as they walked around to the back of the car, Anne winced, imagining how many dents and scratches she had put into the side as the car had ground to a halt in the ditch. Ty flicked back the sides of his coat, resting his hands on his hips as he stared expressionlessly at the Mercedes, but Mike was not inclined to be so silently tactful. He voiced his opinion clearly.

"Have you any idea how much a car like this costs?" he asked sharply, turning toward Anne. "Couldn't you have been more careful, for heaven's sake? I thought everybody knew not to slam on the brakes when driving in snow or ice."

With a defiant uptilting of her chin, Anne glared right back at him. "Can't you be quiet? I don't need you to tell me this is an expensive car. I didn't wreck it deliberately, and I'd appreciate it if you didn't keep trying to make me feel worse than I already do."

"Yes, drop it, Mike. You've said too much already," Ty agreed abruptly, thrusting his hands into his trouser pockets. "It's possible the accident wouldn't have happened if Miss Fairchild hadn't been tired. You were supposed to help her drive."

To his credit, Mike looked somewhat ashamed as he followed Ty back around onto the road. "Well, what now?" he muttered. "Do we just wait here until somebody comes along?"

"No. This road isn't very heavily traveled." Ty inclined his head toward the snow-covered, boulder-scattered meadow that sloped upward beyond the highway. "The house is right up there, just out of sight in that stand of trees at the top of the hill. It won't be a long walk." His dark brows lifted questioningly as he glanced at both Mike and Anne. "Or, you two could climb back into the car and wait here until I can drive back down in the jeep."

Mike's eyes brightened. "We'll wait."

"We'll go," Anne said simultaneously, and when Mike glared at her indignantly, she lifted her shoulders and spread her hands in a resigned gesture. "I'd just rather walk to the house than wait here in the car." A hint of excitement sparkled in her gray eyes. "Come on, a walk in the snow will give us a chance to stretch our legs after sitting in the car all that time. Just think of it as a little adventure, Mike."

Though a smile tugged upward at the corners of Ty's mouth, Mike wasn't amused. Frowning, he looked down at his feet ensconced in obviously new western-style boots. "I'd be nuts to go tramping through a meadow in these boots. They cost me $400."

"They shouldn't leak then," Ty remarked casually, his eyes narrowing enigmatically as he looked at Anne and found her biting her lower lip to fight a smile. Then he stepped past Mike and leaned into the car to pull out Anne's coat.

She slipped her arms into the sleeves as he held it for her. After murmuring her thanks, she stepped away from him again and wrapped the down coat snugly around her. It wasn't elegant. Slick and unwieldy, it took up far too much room in her closet and she suspected she looked like a shiny nylon-clad polar bear in it. But it was warm. And, at the moment, staying warm was more important than trying to appear elegant.

After Ty and Mike had retrieved their own overcoats from the car and put them on, the three of them walked across the road, stopping at the weathered split-rail fence that enclosed the meadow. Anne eyed it with some trepidation, not exactly eager to try to climb a fence in a dress. Apparently her uncertainty transmitted itself to Ty because he suddenly swept her up in his arms and put her down on the other side of the fence, saying softly, "There, that was simple enough, wasn't it?"

Though Anne nodded automatically, his action had been so unexpected that she was temporarily flustered. A blush tingled hotly in her cheeks, and to conceal it, she hastily pulled up her collar and hunched her shoulders, pretending to snuggle her face down in her coat as if she were trying to get warmer. Actually, she no longer felt cold at all, despite the icy wind that buffeted them. The blush that had risen in her cheeks seemed to be spreading heat over her entire body, but she supposed it was only natural to be a little embarrassed. Being swooped up in a man's arms without any warning whatsoever was disconcerting to say the least.

Leaving the fence behind, the three of them began climbing the sloping meadow. Anne had to quicken her pace to keep up with Ty, while Mike lagged along behind them, grumbling every step of the way. When he mumbled something about Anne's lack of driving ability, she stared back over her shoulder, but his head was bent so he didn't notice she was watching him.

"I'm tempted to throw a snowball at him," she murmured, mainly to herself, then smiled apologetically as Ty looked down at her. "But I guess that wouldn't be a very dignified thing for an executive secretary to do, would it?"

"I am surprised at you, Miss Fairchild," he answered quite solemnly, though there was a barely perceptible glint of amusement dancing in his blue eyes. "Considering your very proper, sedate behavior in the office, I wouldn't have imagined you'd ever be tempted to throw a snowball at anyone."

"All of us have our moments of madness, even we sedate secretaries," she retorted mischievously, but her expression almost immediately sobered. "I'm really sorry about your car, Mr. Manning. Mike was right. Hitting the brake was a stupid mistake."

"Accidents happen, Miss Fairchild. If you drove like a maniac the way my sister Jenny sometimes does, I'd have reason to be angry. But you're a competent driver. I blame the icy conditions for this mishap, not you."

"I know, but I still feel terribly guilty about scraping up your car. I'm sure the repairs will be expensive, but perhaps if you kept part of my salary every month, I . . ."

"Don't be ridiculous," he responded tautly, the contours of his lean face hardening with something akin to impatience. "I don't expect you to pay the repair bill. I have insurance."

"Yes, but I still feel responsible."

"Enough," he commanded softly but very emphatically. "Let's just be glad that no one was hurt."

The no-nonsense look in his eyes silenced her effectively, though she might have thanked him for not exacting payment from her if he hadn't become so cool and remote again. As it was, she said nothing else at all while they trudged up the hill.

At last they reached the crest and waited for Mike to catch up before walking on through the grove of bare oak trees. The wind rattled the branches and swayed the tall, full spruces planted in a row before them. When they stepped between two of those bordering evergreens, Ty's house stood before them. Anne liked it. A two-story structure covered with wood shingles, it complemented the surrounding woods rather than detracted from their natural beauty. Gray wisps of smoke drifting from a stone chimney welcomed them as they walked through the wind-driven snow to the stone steps leading to the veranda. Before they could reach the front door, however, it was opened from inside. A tall angular woman with graying hair and a broad friendly face smiled with obvious relief at Ty, as she smoothed her hands over the voluminous white apron she wore.

"Well, I'm glad it's you, Mr. Manning," she announced. "Didn't hear the car and couldn't think who it might be out here stomping around on the porch."

"We were just trying to knock the snow off our shoes, Ellie," Ty said, indicating with a gesture that Anne should precede him into the house. After they were all in and the door was closed behind them, he smiled at Ellie. "Sorry if we startled you, but we walked up. Had a little accident with the car."

Ellie demanded details, and after she had heard exactly what had happened, she shook her head and clicked her tongue against her teeth. "Ain't that a shame. Well, it's just a blessing nobody got hurt. Now, I bet some hot coffee would taste good after that long walk up here. Wouldn't it?" As she herded them along the wide entrance foyer, she smiled sympathetically at Anne. "That wind must be mighty cold. Your cheeks are rosy red, honey."

"Ellie, this is Anne Fairchild, my new secretary," Ty said as they approached the winding staircase that led up to the second floor. "And I don't think you've ever met Mike Bennett. He's one of the lawyers with the firm. Anne, Mike, this is Ellie Caldwell, my housekeeper."

As Ellie gave both visitors a genuine smile of welcome, Anne extended her hand. The housekeeper clasped it firmly, but her warm brown eyes widened and she shook her head and clicked her teeth again when she felt how cold it was. "Goodness, girl, your skin's like ice."

"Maybe you should get Miss Fairchild some coffee and let her take it up to her room. She might like a hot bath," Ty suggested, running his long lean fingers through his thick dark brown hair. "I'll wait and have a cup after I've driven down to the car in the jeep and brought back the luggage."

"But you've just come in from the cold," Ellie protested maternally. "I think you should have some coffee before you go back outside again."

"Later. First, I'm changing my clothes and going back for the luggage," Ty persisted, then took the steps two at a time.

As he disappeared upstairs, Ellie sniffed disapprovingly, then directed Anne and Mike to the antique deacon's bench sitting against a pecan-paneled wall. "Sit a minute and I'll put on a fresh pot of coffee before I show you up to your rooms."

After the housekeeper loped away toward the back of the house, Anne removed her coat and sat down on the bench, watching Mike as he came to join her. "Aren't you going with Mr. Manning?" she asked. "He might need some help with the luggage."

"There are only three suitcases," Mike answered rather shortly, then gave her a sheepish grin. "To tell the truth, these new boots are pinching like crazy. I'll be lucky if I can hobble upstairs."

"New shoes can be murder," Anne agreed pleasantly, while trying to fold her unfoldable coat. "Maybe you should soak your feet. That might help."

"Or, maybe I should invite you to my room and ask you to massage them for me," Mike countered mischievously. "But before I make such a provocative suggestion, I guess I'd be wise to apologize for all the nasty remarks I made about your driving. I didn't mean them. I'm always a real grump when I first wake up."

Anne laughed softly. "Well, that certainly was a rude awakening. I accept your apology. But . . . you'd better ask Ellie to massage your feet because I have to refuse your invitation."

"That's nothing new. You refused my last two dinner

invitations, too," Mike retorted, eyeing her speculatively. "Surely you're not still busy every evening, moonlighting at that dress shop in the mall?" When Anne shook her head, he grinned. "Why was it so important for you to earn some extra money? Were you saving for a down payment on a fancy car or something?"

"Not exactly," Anne evaded. "But as I said, I don't work there anymore. My promotion meant a raise in salary, so I don't have to moonlight, although I actually enjoyed working in the dress shop. It was fun."

"I wouldn't call it fun to work every evening," Mike declared wryly. "I can think of better things to do with my free time. And now that you have your evenings free, what do you do?"

"Relax. Read. Go out with friends," Anne told him. "I can always find something interesting to do with my time."

"And I guess you must be able to go see your mother more often now, too? How is she? And your sisters? Did you ever manage to convince the older one to start college?"

Nodding, Anne breathed a heartfelt sigh of relief. "Yes, I finally persuaded her. She started in January and really enjoys going. And her grades are very good."

Before Mike could speak again, footsteps descending the stairs claimed his attention. Both he and Anne watched as Ty Manning came toward them. Anne's eyes widened slightly. He was dressed more casually than she had ever seen him dress. In jeans and a faded denim shirt, he looked younger and somehow less intimidating. Even so, she gave him a cautious smile as he walked past the deacon's bench, opened the door to the closet beneath the staircase and brought out a brown leather car coat. He returned her smile absently as he put on the coat. "I should be back with our luggage in about fifteen minutes," was all he said before he strode away toward the front door.

He was pulling the door closed behind him when Ellie returned from the kitchen. Without undue ceremony, she ushered Anne and Mike upstairs along a wide, carpeted hallway, stopping to open the second door on the right.

Anne's room was delightful. Pecan-paneled, with plush apricot carpeting and apricot-sprigged muslin curtains that matched the bedspread on the huge mahogany four-poster, it was warm yet spacious. Ellie pointed out the door to the adjoining bathroom, and after she left to show Mike to his room, Anne happily stripped off her clothes and treated herself to a warming bath.

Twenty minutes later, relaxed after a soak in the hot scented water, she left the bathroom, wrapped in a huge body towel. Finding her suitcase had been placed on the wooden chest at the foot of the bed, she shed the towel, shivering slightly as she slipped into her bra and panties. Taking her cue from Ty's casual attire, she put on jeans also and a soft ivory velour shirt. As she stepped into comfortable suede espadrilles, she tried once more to confine that wayward tendril of hair, but it was a futile effort. As the silken strand fell forward again to tickle her cheek, she shook her head and left the room, then drew in a sharp, startled breath as she nearly collided with Ty who was about to enter the room directly across the hall from hers.

They both stopped short. Anne grimaced apologetically. "This just isn't my day. Sorry," she said softly, lifting her eyes to meet the clear blue of his.

He didn't answer. Eyes narrowing, his gaze drifted slowly over the alluring, distinctly feminine curves of her body, covered, but not concealed, by the jeans and velour shirt. Anne tensed under his slow examination, wondering what on earth he could possibly find so interesting about her appearance.

Chapter Two

After several long seconds of Ty's intent scrutiny, Anne's skin began to tingle with uncomfortable warmth. Luckily, before a revealing blush could actually flare in her cheeks, a sudden commotion downstairs claimed Ty's attention.

"Ty, oh, Ty darling," an unpleasantly strident female voice called out. "You're not hurt, are you? We saw the Mercedes in the ditch on our way up here. What in the world happened?"

"Obviously Kirt decided to bring Millicent Beaumont along for the weekend," Ty said unnecessarily, turning back to look at Anne again. "Shall we go down together?"

"I . . . well, no, I've forgotten something," she answered haltingly. "But I'll be down in a few minutes." When he nodded perfunctorily and left her, she hurried back into her room, hastily pulling her shirt off over her head. Convinced Ty had been staring at her because he didn't think jeans were appropriate attire for an executive secretary, she changed to a neat black skirt and white blouse, then replaced the espadrilles with low-heeled black kid pumps.

Sitting down at the vanity, she checked the neatness of the golden coil of hair on her nape, then wrinkled her nose at her reflection in the oval mirror. She wasn't looking forward to the weekend. Millicent Beamont and Kirt Callen weren't her favorite people. She had dealt with Millicent on two occasions in the office, and the woman had always assumed a cool, supercilious demeanor, almost to the point of being snobbish. Tremendously wealthy and active in Washington D.C.'s highest social circles, she seemed to think herself too fine to be friendly to a mere secretary. Separated from her husband, she flitted from one high-society partner to another. Kirt Callen was a fellow member of the elite, so it wasn't surprising that they were together this weekend, though Anne wondered if Millicent might be more interested in Ty Manning than in Kirt. Still, she didn't really dread the weekend because of Millicent Beaumont. Her snobbishness wasn't unduly upsetting.

Anne's dislike of Kirt Callen, however, had nothing to do with snobbery. At first glance, he seemed charming, but it didn't take a great deal of perception to soon realize that his ego was as huge as the grand mansion his father had left him. And he was far too inclined to play up his swinging playboy image. Worse yet, he had wandering hands. Any reasonably attractive female in his vicinity was potential prey. He touched hands, cheek, hair, shoulders and arms with blatant audacity. And when he was being particularly macho, he would brush his body against his victim with self-confident insistence, while smiling down into her eyes as if he thought she should be grateful for his attention. To some, his charm and wealth might appeal, but to Anne he seemed like a fraud. She wasn't fooled by him.

Actually, she disliked him. Although he rarely tried to touch her anymore, because she had once deliberately kicked his shin, she still had no respect for him. Millicent's snobbishness she could tolerate, but Kirt's playboy act irked her. He was the main reason she dreaded the weekend. But business was business. Since Ty handled all Callen's vast property holdings and investments, meetings with him were usually long and Anne's presence was necessary.

Grimacing at the thought of Kirt's wandering hands, Anne got up from the vanity, knowing she couldn't hide in her room forever. She observed herself critically in the cheval glass. Surely, even Ty Manning would agree she looked suitably demure now. When she really dressed up, she knew she could look quite attractive, but in this dark skirt and blouse, she looked just plain average. Stepping closer to the mirror, she shrugged resignedly, never realizing that her creamy ivory complexion, her wide gray eyes framed by thick, long lashes, the soft, full shape of her mouth and the healthy sheen of her honey-gold hair gave her a simple, cameo-like loveliness.

Squaring her shoulders resolutely, she left her room and slowly descended the steps, telling herself she would kick Kirt Callen again if he once tried to corner her during the weekend. Pausing at the foot of the stairs, she heard voices beyond the double doors to the right and went to open them, assuming she was entering the living room. And it was the living room, but one like she had never before seen. Circular, almost completely enclosed in double-paned glass, it was surrounded by the snow-covered evergreens and bare oaks outside. Stepping onto the thick forest-green carpet was almost like stepping out into the woods. Yet, snow was falling outside and the wind was swaying the trees, while inside, in the huge stone fireplace, a roaring blaze provided a homey warmth. The room was simply furnished with antiques and comfortable velvet-covered sofas and chairs in subdued colors of cream and pale gold. Brighter accents were provided by brass and pewter objets d'art and beautiful enameled vases.

Millicent Beamont was poised attractively on one cream sofa, which was a perfect foil for her exotic dark beauty. To further accentuate her dark tan, she wore a white cashmere dress, undoubtedly a designer original. At the moment, she was idly stroking the heavy gold chains she wore around her neck, while swinging one foot, elegantly shod in snakeskin pumps. She was a beautiful woman with thick chestnut hair, a voluptuous figure and slanted green eyes that were presently gleaming with appreciation as she watched Ty.

He, Mike and Kirt Callen were standing by the mahogany bar, and as Anne took another step forward, Ty glanced up and saw her. His brows lifted questioningly as he subjected her to another lingering gaze, but before she could try to interpret the look he gave her, Millicent spied her, too.

"Hello, Miss Fairfax," she drawled, her upper lip curling slightly.

"My name is Fairchild, Anne Fairchild, Mrs. Beaumont," Anne responded politely, completely ignoring the woman's cool, supercilious manner. "How are you?"

"Rather chilly, actually," Millicent said, smoothing her hair. "I certainly didn't expect to run into snow up here, or I would have insisted we hold this meeting someplace else. I can't stand snow, you know."

Anne didn't know and didn't much care but she smiled softly and rested her slender hands on the back of an unoccupied chair. Wondering if the business discussion had already begun, she glanced at Ty, who was still clad in his jeans and denim shirt. As he reached across the bar for a cut-glass tumbler, the muscles of his shoulders tautened the denim fabric, and Anne noticed with inward amusement that Millicent Beaumont seemed fascinated by the sight. But her amusement vanished immediately when Ty turned and met her eyes. He held up the tumbler.

"What would you like to drink, Anne?"

Anne? Her former boss at Manning had always called her Anne, but Ty had consistently called her Miss Fairchild. Until now. And there was something oddly disconcerting in hearing his deep, melodious voice saying her first name. She masked that unreasonable reaction, however, and answered, "Ginger ale would be fine, thank you."

"Anne, my dear, you look beautiful as usual," Kirt Callen declared, making a beeline for her. His darkly tanned face broke into a smile that didn't impress her in the slightest. She stiffened as he approached and had to fight down the desire to sidestep him and walk away. When he lifted one of her slender hands off the back of the chair and held it tightly between both of his, she tried to extract it immediately, but he simply tightened his hold and squeezed her fingers. Finding it impossible to even force a smile, she merely inclined her head in greeting. "Good evening, Mr. Callen," she managed to say politely. "How are you?"

"Superb," he answered, looking her over from head to foot with unabashed intensity. "Especially now that you've joined us."

Ignoring that ridiculous statement, Anne tried to free her hand again, and her gray eyes glittered with impatience when he simply squeezed her fingers again, slowly and suggestively this time. Her impatience only seemed to amuse him, so she assumed a bland expression, hoping feigned indifference would gain her release. It didn't. Callen held onto her hand tenaciously.

Though he wasn't particularly tall or muscular, he was so blatantly aggressive that Anne was uneasy around him. And he was devious. Touching only her hand, he had placed her in a position where she would look foolish if she did anything drastic to make him release her. Certainly, she couldn't kick his shin again, though she ached to do so.

Glancing at Millicent, she found the other woman watching the scene with total indifference, then looking down at her mauve-tipped fingernails with considerably more interest. Obviously, the fact that she had accompanied Kirt up here for the weekend didn't mean there was anything serious between them, because Millicent didn't seem to care one whit that Kirt was silently propositioning Anne right before her eyes.

Anne cared, however. Though Kirt Callen had only been holding her hand about half a minute, the time seemed longer, and she was feeling more uncomfortable by the second. Looking across the room, she tried to catch Mike's eye, but he was too busy spearing an olive for his martini to notice her. Then, beside him, Ty looked up and met her rather wide-eyed gaze. To her surprise, he seemed to read it correctly.

Picking up the glass of ginger ale he had just poured for her, he strode across the room, flicking a cold glance at Kirt Callen. "Here's your drink, Anne," he said quietly, taking her arm as she gave him a grateful little smile. Drawing her gently out of Callen's grasp, he escorted her around the chair. "Wouldn't you like to sit down?"

Composed again, now that she had been rescued, she nodded and settled herself in the cream-colored velvet wing chair. Thanking him for the drink, she took it and had a sip, watching over the rim of the glass as he walked to the stone fireplace, opened the mesh screen, and tossed in another log. After positioning the new log with a poker, he propped one elbow on the stone mantel. Crossing his long, powerful legs at the ankle, he leaned comfortably on the mantel while surveying the living room.

"Well, Kirt, you said someone had given you a tip on some foreign investments," Ty said at last. "Why don't you tell me more about it."

"Oh, don't you dare, Kirt," Millicent commanded, swinging her eyes around to Ty. "Really, darling, must we start discussing business already? You're going to spend most of the weekend going over the details of that shopping center purchase anyway, so . . ."

"I bought the shopping center a month ago," Kirt corrected her imperiously. "This weekend, we're discussing another apartment complex."

"Whatever. It's all deadly dull," Millicent drawled, then gave Ty a beguiling smile. "Surely you don't have to start talking business right this minute, do you?"

"Since Kirt never seems inclined to come to my office to discuss business, we have quite a lot to discuss," Ty responded matter-of-factly. "It's been quite some time since I've brought him up to date on all his investments."

Millicent giggled rather foolishly. "Well, so what? You might as well be speaking Greek when you talk to him about business anyway. I'm sure he's quite content to let you handle everything for him."

"I would like to be brought up to date," Kirt protested, as he tried to light a long, fat cigar. "My financial investments are complex."

Watching as he clamped the cigar between his teeth, Millicent sniffed. "Oh, do stop trying to act like an entrepreneur. You don't know much more about finances than I do. Ty does all the work for you. He finds all the profitable investments."

"Even so, Kirt should know about the investments I make," Ty answered, before Kirt had a chance to make an indignant reply. "It's his money and property we're talking about. I only manage it."

"Yes, darling, I get the point," Millicent countered, pursing her mauve-glossed lips into a silly little pout. "But surely we can just chat awhile before you begin discussing business."

Anne detected the barely perceptible tightening of Ty's jaw and the hint of an impatient gleam that flared for a second in his blue eyes, but at last, he shook his head resignedly and gave the other woman an indulgent smile. "And what would you like to chat about?"

"Ooh, well, I just have scads of gossip to tell," she whispered conspiratorially with a deep-throated chuckle. Patting the sofa cushions beside her, she crooked one finger, beckoning him to her. "Come and sit with me, darling, while I tell you about Scooter and Tippie Bedford. They're clients of yours, aren't they? Well, you'll never believe what I heard about them the other day! Nancy told me . . ."

A half hour later, Anne heaved a sigh of relief when they moved to the dining room. After doing justice to Ellie's trout amandine, rice pilaf and tiny garden peas, she felt considerably better, though somewhat sleepy. Sipping her white wine, she closed her ears to Millicent's inane chatter and relaxed . . . until she felt the hand descend on her knee. Unfortunately, she was seated next to Kirt, and though he had brushed his elbow against her several times during the meal, he hadn't actually laid a hand on her till now. She stiffened, and when he suddenly squeezed her thigh just above her knee, she reacted instinctively. Reaching down, she picked up his hand and flung it from her. His knuckles hit the bottom of the table with a resounding thump, and she felt herself blushing furiously.

Her eyes darted up and met Ty's, and he actually laughed. Or at least he started to, then changed it to a cough. Pressing a snowy white linen napkin to his mouth, he hid a smile, but amusement danced in his eyes as they held Anne's. Obviously, he realized exactly what had happened, though Mike and Millicent appeared thoroughly confused.

"What was that thumping noise?" Millicent questioned. "Don't tell me you have ghosts in the house, Ty. That thump sounded as if it came from under the table, just like the tapping I heard at a séance I attended several weeks ago. I must confess I was really scared. Nancy's medium conducts her séances in an old house on Front Street, and it was really a terribly depressing place."

By now, Ty's amusement was becoming infectious. Anne had to fight back a smile, no easy accomplishment when she glanced at Kirt and found him massaging his knuckles and wearing a petulant scowl. He made no attempt to touch her again, however, so she was able to enjoy the raspberry torte Ellie served for dessert.

When they returned to the living room for coffee, it was past nine o'clock. The long day and the hours of driving unfamiliar, winding roads were combining to make Anne weary. She was relieved when Ty announced that it was too late to start their business discussion. They would make faster progress in the morning when everyone was well-rested.

His announcement pleased Millicent immensely. Paying Kirt scant attention and pointedly ignoring

Anne, she focused all her energies on Ty and Mike. Obviously a woman who enjoyed trying to impress attractive men, she told them about the ballet troupe her women's club wanted to sponsor and dropped the names of several important artists and sculptors she knew. All the while, she included Mike by touching his hand occasionally, but it was Ty she seemed more intent on impressing.

All in all, it was a boring evening, but just as Anne thought she was surely going to fall asleep in her chair, there was a commotion out in the foyer. A moment later a girl of about eighteen sauntered into the living room. Anne recognized the pretty teenager as Ty's younger sister Jenny, whom she had met once at the office. On that occasion she had seemed a nice enough girl. Tonight, however, something must have been bothering her, judging by the rather defiant expression on her face. Languidly, she strolled across the room, her hands slipped into the back pockets of snugly fitting designer jeans. "Surprise, everybody," she said liltingly, stopping beside Anne's chair. "Guess you didn't expect to see me here, did you, Ty?"

If Ty was surprised, he concealed it admirably. Subjecting his sister to a long, steady stare, he asked calmly, "What's brought you up here, Jenny? I thought you planned to spend the weekend with your friend Beth. Wasn't she having a big party?"

Jenny turned up her nose rather disdainfully. "I changed my mind about going. My friends are really silly sometimes. They're beginning to bore me." Running her fingers through her hair, she abruptly changed the subject. "The snow's really coming down out there. But would you believe I made it up here in less than two and a half hours?"

"And how did you accomplish that daring feat?" Ty

asked flatly, though his hardening expression conveyed disapproval. "Surely you didn't try driving through this snowstorm in your MG?"

"No. I borrowed Charlie's jeep. And I think maybe you should have borrowed one too, considering what happened to the Mercedes. I can't believe *you,* of all people, drove off into a ditch."

"He didn't," Anne spoke up compulsively. "I was driving."

"Oh, really?" Sounding almost disappointed, Jenny smiled sardonically at her brother. "Well, I should have known you weren't responsible. You never make mistakes, do you, Ty?"

Though Ty ignored her slightly sarcastic tone, he folded his arms across his broad chest, watching her intently. "I have a feeling you're going to wish you'd gone to Beth's party, after all. I'm afraid you're going to be much more bored up here. We're going to be discussing business all weekend."

Shrugging, Jenny ambled across the room and trailed her fingers along the mahogany-topped bar as she walked behind it. Her eyes, as blue as her brother's, seemed to be issuing a challenge as she looked back at him. "I'd like a drink, but I suppose you'll insist I have something insipid like a soft drink or fruit juice?"

"You know the answer to that," Ty replied, his voice deceptively soft, as impatience tightened his jaw. "Have a ginger ale."

Jenny glowered at him. "Thanks, but no thanks. I'd rather have nothing at all than have that," she proclaimed with a rebellious toss of her head. When her brother simply ignored her belligerence and turned back to Millicent, Jenny moved restlessly around the room.

Anne watched her, noticing the slight downward

curve of her mouth and suspecting that something more serious than a mere tiff with her older brother was causing her unhappiness. Her tension seemed nearly tangible. Wandering around the room, she picked up a brass statuette, then put it back down on a side table with more force than was necessary. Moving on, she stopped for a moment to stare morosely at the snow still falling outside the glass-enclosed room. Twirling a strand of her long dark hair, she prodded the nap of the plush carpet with her toe and sighed deeply, as if she didn't quite know what to do with herself.

Sensing that an underlying sadness had brought on the girl's rebellious behavior, Anne felt a rush of compassion for her, then realized she was not the only person in the room who was surveying Jenny with interest. Leaving his chair, Kirt Callen strolled across the room to where she stood. Glancing over his shoulder at Ty and finding himself unobserved, he whispered something into Jenny's ear, then pressed the cut-glass tumbler he carried into her hand.

For a second, Jenny looked surprised. Then, giving Kirt a conspiratorial smile, she turned so that her brother couldn't see what she was doing and took a large swallow of the amber-colored liquid. Though her face suddenly became flushed, she managed to suppress a cough and forced herself to take another smaller sip of the drink, before handing the glass back to Kirt.

As he deliberately brushed his hand over Jenny's during the exchange, Anne gritted her teeth, feeling a nearly overwhelming desire to get up and push him through one of the huge plate glass windows. During the five minutes that followed, unfortunately, that desire intensified Playboy that he was, he took full advantage of Jenny's obvious discontent, despite the fact that he was far too old for her. More disturbing than that was the realization that Jenny seemed to welcome his attentions. As he talked softly to her and occasionally touched her face and hair, she became more animated, obviously flattered by what he was saying and too young to see what a fraud he was.

Anne looked at Ty, hoping he would notice what was happening and do something to get Jenny out of Kirt's clutches. But Millicent, babbling away non-stop, was sitting forward on the sofa, blocking Ty's view of his sister. With an inward sigh, Anne turned back to watch Jenny again. A frown knitted her brow as she saw Kirt slip the girl his glass again. After taking a sip, Jenny glanced surreptitiously over her shoulder. Her eyes met Anne's, and as she apparently decided Anne's frown conveyed disapproval of her, she stiffened her shoulders defiantly. Her blue eyes glittered icily, issuing a silent challenge as she moved forward one step.

"Well, well, Miss Fairchild, I guess you're enjoying seeing how the other half lives," she said loudly enough for everyone in the room to hear. "Or are you feeling a little out of place?" She attempted an encouraging smile that failed miserably. "You shouldn't feel uncomfortable, you know, just because Millicent's all decked out in an expensive designer original and you're dressed in your plain little black skirt and off-the-rack blouse."

Though Anne heard Ty's muffled imprecation, she didn't seek his help. Being a secretary for five years had taught her how to deal with rudeness, and she was quite capable of handling Jenny herself. As she touched the collar of her pristine white blouse, she gave the girl one of her warmest smiles. "Oh, do you like my blouse? I think it's nice, too. And would you believe I got it on sale for half price?"

For a fleeting instant Jenny seemed startled that her

attempt to embarrass Anne had failed, but she recovered quickly. With a disgruntled sniff, she turned around to stare out the window again.

At least the incident had made Ty aware of Kirt's interest in his sister, and he ended their private little discussion immediately. Without being the least bit obvious, he made certain Kirt was drawn into the conversation he was having with Millicent, so that finally the other man had no choice except to leave Jenny and return to his chair.

After that, the time dragged by, at least for Anne. Jenny plopped down on a bar stool and stared sullenly at the floor, while Mike tried valiantly to keep his eyes from fluttering shut. Realizing he must be finding Millicent as boring as she was, Anne smiled to herself and shifted restlessly in her chair. Finally, she could stand the woman's inane chatter no longer and resolved to be the first to make her excuses and go up to bed.

Standing, she smiled politely at Ty. "If you'll excuse me, Mr. Manning, I think I'll go upstairs now. It's been a long day."

His gaze narrowed and he intently surveyed her face for a moment before finally nodding. Even as Anne left the room, she felt he was still watching her, though she had no idea why he should be. She finally decided weariness was making her over-imaginative. Yawning behind one hand, she climbed the stairs and was halfway down the hall to her room, when Ty called her name.

She stopped and turned, watching him approach with a questioning smile. Her smile faded slowly as she saw the grim expression on his face.

"I want to apologize for my sister's rudeness, since she's in no mood to apologize for herself," he announced abruptly, his magnetic blue eyes piercing the gray luminosity of hers. "I hope she's not the reason you decided to come upstairs."

"Oh no," Anne assured him honestly. "I really am tired. Jenny didn't upset me. I could see something was bothering her."

Massaging the back of his neck with one lean hand, Ty nodded. "She's going through a difficult time right now but, still, that's no excuse for her behavior."

"Please don't worry about it," Anne insisted, then smiled understandingly. "I have two younger sisters myself. One of them is eighteen, and sometimes she would try the patience of a saint. Besides, I remember what it is to be eighteen—life can seem extremely complicated."

"How very old and wise you sound, Miss Fairchild," he said, his expression softening as he gave her a teasing smile. "And how long ago was it that you were eighteen?"

"Long enough," she answered pertly. "In today's world, a person learns a great deal in five years. So just give Jenny time. Maybe whatever is bothering her tonight will soon be forgotten."

"I'm afraid it might not be so simple," he said cryptically, then escorted Anne down the hall to her room and opened her door. "I'll have Ellie call you at about seven in the morning. Goodnight, Anne."

As he turned to walk away, she gave in to a sudden compulsion and laid her hand on his forearm. Even when she felt his muscles tauten beneath her fingers and a shiver of apprehension trickle along her spine, she had to speak up. "This is none of my business, Mr. Manning, but . . . well, I noticed that Jenny seemed to be a little impressed with Kirt Callen, and I'm sure you wouldn't want her to. . . . Oh, you know what I'm saying. He's such a . . ."

When she didn't allow herself to finish what would have been a very uncomplimentary description, Ty laughed softly. "I know exactly what you're saying and you're right. I'll see to it that Jenny stays away from him. Perhaps I should send her to you for lessons on how to handle a man like Kirt. You seemed quite proficient at putting him in his place at dinner tonight."

A satisfied smile hovered on her softly shaped lips. As his eyes darkened abruptly and moved slowly over her upturned face, they lingered on the wayward strand of hair that brushed her temple. Almost involuntarily, his hand came up. His fingers slipped beneath the wispy tendril, lifting it out slightly.

"You just can't keep it confined, can you?" he asked, his voice low and unusually husky. "I've seen you tuck it back a million times in the past two weeks, but it always falls back to graze your cheek."

"It's a nuisance," Anne breathed, her heart beating with dizzying rapidity. "I don't think I'll ever get it to stay where it belongs."

"Then stop trying," he commanded softly, his eyes holding hers as he gently lowered the silken tendril, then released it.

As he moved his hand away, his warm fingers brushed lightly against Anne's cheek, and it took all of her self-control not to react to the unexpected touch. His fingers almost seemed to burn her skin. Instead, she simply murmured goodnight, stepped into her room and closed the door behind her. Her hand shook slightly as she reached up to touch the loose strand of honey-gold hair. For several long seconds, she stood by the door immobile, recalling the blueness of Ty's eyes, the tan smoothness of his skin and the strong contours of his lean face. Then, regaining her common sense, she shook her head and berated herself for such foolish thoughts. Ty might be acting a little more friendly, but he was still her boss and that was all he would ever be. She meant to make certain of that.

Chapter Three

The next morning, Anne was awake early. Before Ellie could come to call her, she was dressed and downstairs, planning on a quick walk before breakfast. After getting her coat from the foyer closet, she slipped her small hands into brown suede gloves, opened the back door and stepped outside onto the snow-covered terrace.

Though the sky was still overcast and gray, the snow was falling more slowly. Fat flakes fluttered down on the silent countryside. During the night, freezing rain had encased the shrubs and branches of trees in glittering ice and had formed a crust on the carpet of snow. Anne's boots crunched through the surface as she walked through a stand of bare oaks, their large trunks draped by drifting snow. Taking deep breaths of the fresh clean air, she wandered farther from the house to the edge of a wood that stretched out for some distance, then came to an abrupt halt as she spied a deer several yards ahead, foraging for what food he could find at the base of a tall pine. Perhaps he sensed her presence because he raised his head and stared at her, his soft brown eyes conveying more curiosity than fear. Anne stood perfectly still, admiring the buck's handsome antlers as he looked her over for several moments. When he apparently decided she meant to do him no harm and began to search around the roots of the tree for food again, she smiled and continued to watch him.

Suddenly, he jerked his head up and, with a powerful leap, bounded away through the woods. Wondering what had frightened him off, Anne glanced around curiously, then grinned as she saw the reason for the buck's abrupt flight. Loping toward her from the house was a great golden dog, its massive paws crunching lightly through the crusty snow and kicking up soft clouds of white. Coming to a dead stop at the edge of the wood near Anne, the dog stood at attention, watching the buck disappear among the trees. After issuing one deep-throated bark that sounded more playful than menacing, the golden dog turned its attention to Anne. Its big tail began a steady wagging, swishing across the icy surface of the snow as it unhesitatingly sniffed the gloved hand Anne extended.

Though she knew that the animal was big and powerfully built, Anne knelt down and proceeded to make a lifelong friend by scratching behind the silken ears. The dog sighed happily, and a distinct dreaminess softened its black eyes as it moved its head slowly back and forth beneath Anne's ministering fingers. When Anne stopped the scratching, the dog inexplicably turned around, then gazed back expectantly. It was obvious the animal wanted something Anne was not giving, but unable to interpret that longing gaze, Anne spread her hands in a helpless gesture.

"I don't know what it is you want. Sorry," she said aloud, then gave a soft gasp of surprise when someone directly behind her spoke. Still on her knees, she twisted around and stared up at Ty, who stood towering above her.

"Goldie tends to be very demanding," he said, smiling pleasantly. "She is politely telling you that she now expects her rump to be scratched, too."

Anne laughed and, after stroking Goldie's sleek-coated flanks, gave her the requested scratching. Once that was finished, the dog gave a puppyish wiggle, greeting Ty with the uninhibited affection animals give exclusively to their owners. After sprawling down in the snow and rolling around a bit to express her joy, Goldie leaped up to dash back and forth in front of Anne and Ty, burrowing her soft black nose into the snow, obviously issuing an invitation to play.

"She's a lovely dog," Anne commented, smiling at her antics. "And so friendly."

"And full of energy," Ty added, cupping Anne's elbow in one ungloved hand. "Let's walk. She'll run on ahead of us and expend some of that excess energy."

There was little wind, so the cold was not unbearable as Anne and Ty walked along the edge of the trees down a gentle incline. When they reached a narrow brook that crossed their path, Ty automatically took Anne's hand to help her across. To her surprise, he didn't release her and a moment later, she was glad he hadn't. Somehow, she managed to hook the toe of her boot on a fallen tree limb, half-buried in the snow, and was unable to regain her balance. Ty's lean fingers tightened around her hand, while his free arm quickly encircled her waist, and suddenly she found herself being held very close against him. Instinctively, she had reached up to grasp his shoulder and her cheek brushed his coat. Inhaling the rich, clean scent of leather, she looked up at him, feeling a most idiotic desire to touch her gloved fingers against the strong tanned column of his throat where it rose above his black turtleneck sweater.

Suddenly, her breath caught in her throat, as his arm around her drew her nearer. She could feel his warmth and the taut hardness of his muscular thighs straining against her own. Her eyes darted up and met the piercing, compelling blue of his.

He said nothing. After releasing her, they walked on, though he did catch her hand in his again. More than a little disconcerted by the physical awareness that had begun to develop between them, Anne tried to ease the tension by commenting lightly, "You really must think I'm terribly inept. Yesterday, I couldn't drive, and today, I can't walk."

"I've just been watching the tow truck pull the Mercedes out of the ditch. I thought you'd be glad to know there's very little damage," Ty said, his strong fingers curving more securely around her hand. "We'll be able to drive it back to Alexandria."

"You and Mike will be able to drive it back to Alexandria," Anne said emphatically. "But not me. I don't intend to ever drive any vehicle more expensive than my old rattletrap, secondhand jalopy, not that I think you'd ever ask me to be your chauffeur again."

"As my secretary, you undoubtedly will have to drive the Mercedes again," Ty said, his tone cool and strictly professional once more. "And I did tell you that I don't blame you for the accident, so I think it's time to let the subject drop. Agreed? If you insist on apologizing again and again, I'll have to retaliate by repeatedly saying I'm sorry for Jenny's rudeness last night."

"Oh, but I told you that I didn't expect any apology from you," Anne insisted, looking up into his lean brown face. "I could see she was upset about something. And if you don't mind my saying so, she seemed a bit annoyed at you. Of course, spats between brothers and sisters are inevitable."

"This isn't your ordinary spat though," Ty began softly. "Her resentment toward me is just her way of hiding feelings that are far more painful. You know our father died last year in a boating accident. He and Jenny were very close. Actually, he treated her like a princess, and when he died, she just couldn't cope with life without him. She began having problems in school and with her friends. Unfortunately, Mother was in no condition to help her because she, too, was devastated by losing Dad. With Jenny, she either burst into tears or threatened to turn her over her knee, so I had to step in. But I'm afraid my sister doesn't care for me in the role of a surrogate father. In her mind, I'm only a brother, so I have no right to even give her advice, much less make rules."

Anne nodded sympathetically, sad memories darkening her gray eyes. "It's so difficult to lose your father. My dad died when I was seventeen, so I know what Jenny's feeling. But she should remember that you've lost your father, too. Perhaps you could suggest your mother remind her of that fact."

"Mother's gone to France to stay with a friend for a few months, because, frankly, she and Jenny were fighting incessantly. Jenny has decided that since she no longer has a father, she must be an adult. She tries to act far more sophisticated than she is. Maybe she's trying to transfer her unhappiness to everybody else by being rebellious, but, of course, she's hurting herself more than anyone else."

"I'm sure she'll realize that soon."

"I hope so," Ty said rather doubtingly. "But she can be a very obstinate girl, and I think sometimes she wants to avoid accepting the fact that our father's gone." His expression was pensive as he looked down at Anne. "You were her age when your father died. Did you go through a period of rebellion?"

Gazing at the high rolling hills in the distance, veiled by the blue translucent haze that gave the Blue Ridge its name, Anne shook her head. "We all were terribly hurt when he died, of course, but our lives changed so drastically that we really didn't have time to rebel against what had happened. We were forced to cope. Our farm was mortgaged, even our house, so Mom sold the land. But that still left the mortgage payments on the house that had to be met. She went back to work as a kindergarten teacher. And although I had been accepted at a college, I went to business school instead and got a job. So, maybe in a way, I was luckier than Jenny. My whole life changed and I had to adjust to it."

Ty's eyes narrowed and he searched her face for a long moment. "I think you're being too kind. Jenny should be grateful that her lifestyle hasn't changed. At least she has no financial worries."

"She takes financial security for granted. So did I, until it was gone," Anne explained quietly. "Don't be too hard on her. She is just a child."

"So were you, when your father died."

"I grew up fast, but probably only because I had to," Anne admitted candidly. "I still miss my father, but I discovered very soon that life has to go on. And Jenny will realize that, too, in time. Just be patient with her."

Ty stopped by the line of spruce trees that surrounded his house. His fingers tightened round Anne's hand, and he turned her to face him. "And if everything hadn't changed for you and you could have gone to college, what were you planning to do with your life?"

Anne suddenly grinned. "Maybe I shouldn't say. For

some reason, people seemed surprised when I mention that I once wanted to attend medical school and go into research."

Ty didn't smile. "I'm sorry you weren't able to do it."

"Oh, don't be. I try to believe that everything works out for the best in the end," she answered honestly, her tone matching the low seriousness of his. "My mother and my sisters and I are all very close now, because we went through a difficult time together, and our relationship is very precious to me."

Ty's gaze held hers. "And so you're happy?"

Anne hesitated, searching her own consciousness. "I'm mainly content, but I have many happy moments," she finally answered rather evasively. Then she smiled. "Like now. At the moment, I'm happy because snow always makes me happy." She looked out over the rolling carpet of white that sloped down a gentle incline to the far side of the house. "But I could really be ecstatic, if we had a sled to ride down that hill. It's been ages since I've been sledding."

"Your wish is my command, Miss Fairchild," Ty replied to her astonishment, gesturing toward a small shed beside the multi-car garage. Still holding her hand, he strode away in that direction, walking at such a brisk pace that she had to nearly run to keep up with him. At the shed, he opened the door, leaned inside, then brought out a well-used sled, its red frame scratched and its wooden slats somewhat bleached, but still strong and sturdy. "Ellie's grandchildren use it," he explained. "But I don't think they'd mind if we borrowed it for awhile."

Anne eyed the sled. It would be fun to go swooshing down a snowy hill again but . . . She looked up at Ty. "We don't really have to do this, you know. You did say that you wanted to start working early this morning."

Pulling back the sleeve of his coat, he looked at his thin gold wristwatch. "It's only eight o'clock. And since Kirt probably won't get up until after ten or so, you and I will still have time to have breakfast and get organized after we go sledding. You said a sled ride would make you ecstatic, and I would very much like to see you ecstatic, Miss Fairchild."

His tone was only partially teasing, and Anne felt warmth tingle in her cheeks. Following, as he pulled the sled toward the slope, she wished she had never mentioned sledding. She did love snow and it did make her happy, but perhaps she shouldn't have expressed a desire to go sledding. It certainly wasn't in keeping with the dignified, strictly businesslike image she tried to project in the office. When Ty stopped at the top of the slope and handed her the rope attached to the sled, she smiled wanly.

"Well, what's stopping you?" he prompted. "There's the hill and here's the sled. Go ahead."

She wanted to go, but felt too self-conscious. Shaking her head, she handed the rope back to him. "I'd feel silly, knowing you were standing up here watching," she told him candidly. "So, I don't go, if you don't go with me. Besides, it's no fun sledding alone."

"But you won't be alone," Ty replied wryly, inclining his head toward Goldie. The dog was sniffing the sled with avid interest and, at last, politely hopped up onto it and sat down, obviously ready to go. "She always rides down with Ellie's grandchildren, so she'll go with you."

"Look, why don't we just forget the whole thing?" Anne murmured weakly. "I was really half kidding when I said I'd like to go sledding. I didn't expect you to take me seriously."

"Oh, but I did," Ty persisted, catching her hand

again and impelling her toward the sled. "And if I have to go with you to get you to go, then so be it."

Goldie was not happy about this new turn of events, but at Ty's command, she jumped off the sled, her ears drooping in disappointment. But, as Anne sat down on the wooden slats and Ty got on the sled behind her, the dog began to watch with alert excitement.

A most curious sensation weakened Anne's limbs as Ty placed his feet on the steering bar, then reached around her for the rope. She felt surrounded, and the fact that her back was pressed against his hard broad chest did nothing for her equilibrium. His hands lightly brushed her thighs as he held the rope out of the way of the runners, and she impulsively reached out for it. "Let me hold that," she said, her voice slightly squeaky. "Since you don't have gloves on, your hands must be freezing."

"And what do you suggest I do with them, Miss Fairchild?" he asked softly, very close to her ear. There was a hint of amusement in his low voice. "I don't suppose you'd allow me to put them in your coat pockets so I can hold onto you and keep them warm at the same time, would you?"

Anne turned her head to look at him and, finding his dark, lean face disturbingly close to her own, she unconsciously moistened suddenly dry lips with the tip of her tongue. Knowing she would look foolish if she refused his request, she swallowed with some difficulty, then forced herself to say, "Why not? Seems like a logical solution."

Logic, however, had nothing to do with the sudden lurch of her heart as his hands slipped into her pockets and curved firmly around her slender waist. She tensed involuntarily. Even through the thin fabric of the pocket and the yarn of her sweater, she could feel his long fingers brushing over her stomach, and it was as if he had touched bare skin. Luckily, she had no time to analyze her reaction because at that moment, he pushed off with one foot, and they were suddenly speeding down the slope. Goldie bounded along beside, appearing to find as much fun in chasing a sled as in riding on one. And after they came to a stop at the bottom, Ty did allow the dog to ride when he pulled the sled back up to the top.

After a few more runs, Anne had relaxed completely. As they swooped down over the rolling terrain, she laughed, uncaring that the chill wind nipped her cheeks, leaving them rosy-pink. But suddenly Goldie, overly exuberant, bounded directly into their path, and when Ty turned the sled sharply to avoid hitting her, it turned over, dumping them into the snow where they rolled over a couple of times before coming to a complete stop.

Unhurt, Anne was laughing, until she opened her eyes and looked up at Ty, who was practically lying on top of her. But when she abruptly realized that her slender legs were entangled with his long ones, the situation no longer seemed funny. Warned by the light that flared in the depths of his blue eyes, she moved restlessly beneath him, but that did not stop him from cupping her face in his hands and winding the wayward strand of hair that had escaped her hat around one lean finger. Then he lowered his head.

"No," she breathed.

But Ty only smiled softly. Then his lips touched hers, warm and hard, yet disarmingly gentle. Too surprised to resist, she was perfectly still until his kiss became more insistently demanding. When the deepening pressure of his hard lips parted the softness of hers and sent a quickening thrill of pleasure through her body, she was astounded by her own intense response. Dragging her mouth away from the enticing warmth of his, she pushed at his chest and scrambled out from beneath him. Determined not to reveal the effect his kiss had had, she made a great show of adjusting her hat, while saying softly, "I seem to have forgotten for a minute a rule I learned long ago: never kiss the boss. And that's a rule that makes a great deal of sense to me, Mr. Manning."

"I'm sure it does," he answered, getting to his feet and pulling her up to stand before him. Tilting her chin up with one finger, he made her look at him, and there seemed to be a hint of indulgent amusement dancing in his eyes. "But we both know some rules aren't easy to follow, don't we, Anne?"

Unwilling to answer such a provocative question, she moved away, and as they walked up the hill again, she found it impossible to look directly at him. It was hard to believe that just yesterday she had only known him as the cool, brusque businessman she had seen every day in the two weeks she'd been working for him. But today, she knew he was much more complex than that. He cared deeply about his sister and worried about her; with Anne herself, he had exhibited friendliness and a surprising respect for her thoughts and feelings. And when he had kissed her, she had sensed an underlying passion in him that might prove to be quite awesome if unleashed. That made him a dangerous man, and she now had to wonder if she should regret the fact that in the past twenty-four hours, she had begun to genuinely like him for the person that he was.

Chapter Four

Monday in Alexandria was damp and chilly. Anne felt oddly discontent all day and, by the evening, she was glad she had accepted Mike Bennett's invitation to dinner. She needed to be with someone like him, someone entertaining and intelligent, yet in no way threatening. That morning, when he had asked her to a concert and dinner, she had decided on the spur of the moment that it would be good for her to go out with him.

She had even gone so far as to buy herself a new dress, a black sheath of real silk crepe de chine, which she had luckily found on sale. Her conscience had pricked her slightly when she paid the clerk, because she normally saved every extra penny to help with her sister Sue's college expenses. But, just this once, it seemed important to give herself a present, because, since the weekend at Ty's mountain house, she had been feeling strangely restless.

Even now, as she waited for Mike to arrive, she sat on the window seat in her quaint, old-fashioned apartment and stared rather morosely at the tree-lined street below. Normally, she felt content at home, finding pleasure in the high ceilings and wainscoted walls of her rooms. She preferred living here in this once-fashionable old home that had been converted into apartments. Though most of her contemporaries sought apartment complexes offering swimming pools, saunas and tennis courts, Anne was happy here without all those recreational facilities.

At least, she was usually happy, but tonight she felt considerably less content and she knew why. The memory of Ty's kiss hadn't diminished as she had hoped it would. Still disturbed by her own response to his touch, she was rather displeased with herself. She simply couldn't forget the lesson her first employer had taught her when she was eighteen, just out of business college. And the lesson was that getting involved with the boss was the prelude to pain and humiliation.

Strumming her fingers on the windowsill, she resolved firmly to cease these foolish thoughts about Ty Manning. Certainly, he had already forgotten the kiss they had shared, and if he could forget it, so could she. Despite that resolve, it was still a relief when Mike arrived a few minutes later. Forced to turn her thoughts to him, she relegated Ty to the back of her mind and smiled as Mike complimented her on the new dress with an exaggerated wolf whistle.

As Anne allowed him to drape her cashmere stole over her shoulders, she commented offhandedly, "I've never been to the Kennedy Center before, so I'm really looking forward to this evening."

"Let's go then. We'll have dinner first, because I remember you don't like late evenings on weeknights."

He grimaced playfully. "You're too much the perfect employee to go in to work sleepy."

She grinned. "A real party pooper, that's me."

"But a very pretty one," he replied boldly, taking her arm to escort her from her apartment.

Dinner was enjoyable and relaxing, and the concert was very entertaining, but, unfortunately, while leaving Kennedy Center, Anne and Mike encountered Ty and his date for the evening in the lobby. Resplendent in an ivory satin designer gown and a luxurious mink stole, Millicent Beaumont flicked a rather amused gaze over Anne's less extravagant attire. With her barely audible greeting, she conveyed her boredom at running into two such unfashionable, unimportant creatures as Anne and Mike. Ty, however, seemed more interested in talking to them, much to Anne's discomfort. She tensed when he actually suggested that she and Mike join Millicent and him for dinner. When Mike explained that they had already dined, Anne apparently didn't sufficiently disguise her relief, because Ty's gaze suddenly grew cold as it swept swiftly over her.

"Remember we have a busy morning tomorrow, Anne," were his parting words as he and Millicent started to move away. "In fact, I think you should plan to get to the office early."

Nodding, Anne returned his murmured goodnight, then forced herself to smile up at Mike as they, too, made their way through the mingling crowd in the lobby. Later, at her apartment, Mike showed some desire to come in with her, but she diplomatically reminded him that she had to be at work early the next morning. Yet when he left her, she almost wished she'd asked him in for a cup of coffee. Already, she was beginning to feel discontent again. The evening out certainly hadn't lifted her spirits, and it didn't help to realize that her feelings of restlessness had increased the moment she had seen Ty with Millicent.

While Anne was driving to work the next morning, her long-suffering, old car at last gave up the ghost. Without any warning at all of its imminent demise, it simply and quietly went dead while Anne was waiting for a light to turn green. Despite everything she tried, the engine wouldn't start again. In the line of traffic behind her, motorists began to irritably beep their horns. She waved them around her, as she continued to turn the key in the ignition, but to no avail. The engine wouldn't even give a sick cough. Luckily, there was a gas station just down the block, so after glancing at her wristwatch to see how much time she still had to get to work, she walked for help. Unfortunately, the station attendants were all busy, and it was nearly fifteen minutes before one of them was able to help her.

Back at the car a few moments later, the man bent over to get a better look at the inner workings. Then he straightened again, shaking his head. "She's an old one, ain't she? Hard to tell what's the matter with her. Just have to tow her in and take a proper look. But I have to tell you, miss, an old car like this might take a lot of fixing. Might cost you more than it's worth."

Anne sighed, then took a pen and a piece of paper from her purse. "Here's the number where you can reach me all day," she told the man. "After you get an idea of how much work needs to be done, call me and we'll decide whether it's worth it."

Nodding, he gave her a sympathetic smile and took the ignition key she handed him. As he ambled back toward the station to get the tow truck, Anne rushed across the street to the corner where the downtown bus stopped. Though it came only a short time later, she was still twenty minutes late, as she rushed into the modern building where she worked and took the elevator up.

Manning Consultants occupied the entire seventh floor, and when Anne swept off the elevator, Betsy, the young brunette receptionist, grinned cheekily. "Well, will wonders never cease?" she commented wryly. "I've worked here for nearly a year, and I've never once seen you come in late, Anne."

"I guess there's a first time for everything," Anne replied ruefully as she sped past the girl on her way to the carved double doors that opened into her office. After she hastily tossed her purse into her desk drawer, she went to open the ice-blue drapes that covered the tinted glass wall. Light flooded the large room, reflected in the buffed wood surfaces of her desk and the frames of a matching sofa and chairs. Pausing to take a deep breath and to swipe back that aggravating strand of hair, she surveyed her own reflection in the mirror on the wall above the sofa. Except for the fact that her cheeks were unusually flushed, she looked normal. After straightening the skirt of her dark blue suit, she snatched up her steno pad and pencil, then knocked once on the double doors behind her desk.

Without waiting for a response from within, she entered Ty's office, smiling apologetically as he looked up from his teakwood desk and watched her walk toward him. "I'm sorry I'm late, Mr. Manning," she said, the breathlessness caused by her haste, increasing considerably as his blue eyes swept a long gaze slowly over her.

"Maybe if you didn't stay out until all hours, you could get here on time," he practically growled at her, his face hard. "Don't let this happen again, Anne. I won't tolerate tardiness."

"I do have an excuse," she replied stiffly, biting back an angry retort. Her cheeks rosy with indignation and chagrin, she glared back at him. Then, because it was his custom to dictate letters first thing in the morning, she flounced down on the chair before his desk and opened her steno pad as she continued tersely, "I want you to know I'm not late because I was out until all hours—I wasn't. It just so happens that my car went dead at a stoplight and wouldn't start again. I had to get a mechanic to look at it, but he had to tow it to his garage. So I had to wait for a bus, and that's why I'm late. But it *won't* happen again."

As Ty laughed shortly, she jerked up her head, frowning at his rather mocking look.

"Is something funny?" she asked sharply. "Personally, I see nothing amusing in my car going on the blink."

"Neither do I. But I've never seen you out of sorts before," he explained sardonically. "Did you know that your eyes turn a fascinating stormy gray when you're irritated?"

"No, I didn't know. Thanks for sharing such valuable information," she murmured heatedly, in no mood to try to analyze his cryptic comment. Yet, as his eyes narrowed, she felt some regret for giving him such an impertinent answer. Hastily looking away from him, she stared down at the steno pad in her lap, becoming increasingly breathless as she felt his burning gaze searing her. After several long, uneasy moments, while her skin flushed with uncomfortable heat, he at last began dictating his first letter, to her immense relief.

After the dictation ended, Anne returned to her own office to type the letters, and the rest of the morning passed quickly. It was after twelve, as she was at the bank of filing cabinets removing the portfolios Ty would need for his afternoon appointments, when he strode out of his inner office, his dark brown suit jacket flung back over one shoulder. Stopping to button the matching vest he wore, he didn't return the uneasy smile she gave him. Yet, before she could turn and open another file drawer, one large brown hand came out and stayed hers.

"I want you to go to lunch with me, Anne," he commanded rather than requested, "to discuss the details of the overnight trip I'll be making to New York at the end of the week."

Knowing the details of this forthcoming trip weren't complex enough to take much time to discuss, she was surprised he wanted to take her to lunch for that purpose. And she certainly had no desire to go with him after the way he had treated her that morning. With a sweeping gesture encompassing the papers on her desk, she shrugged, unable to look directly at him. "I have a lot of work. I was thinking of skipping lunch altogether."

"But you're not going to," he pronounced flatly. "I want to discuss the trip . . . if you don't mind."

"I'd rather not go," she replied recklessly. "You insinuated this morning that I was failing in my duties here. I'd rather skip lunch and work, so maybe I can begin to make a good impression."

Her slight sarcasm obviously irritated him immensely. His eyes glittered like shards of ice as he took one menacing step toward her. When he spoke, his voice possessed that deceptive softness that she immediately recognized as dangerous. "You seem to be forgetting that I'm the boss here, Anne. If you want to impress me, you'd be wise to start remembering. Now, we will go to lunch and discuss my trip like adults, not like a couple of feuding children. Is that clear?"

It was, and she had no choice except to get her purse and go with him. Twenty minutes later in the plush splendor of one of Alexandria's best restaurants, Anne jotted down one last note pertaining to Ty's trip. After replacing her small notebook in a leather-lined compartment in her purse, she took a tiny sip of chilled white wine, glad that discussing business details had helped ease the tension between them. More relaxed than she'd thought she would be, she glanced around the elegant dining room. Suddenly her lips thinned to a grim line when she noticed a man and girl in a secluded corner exchange a lingering kiss. Wondering if the couple thought the potted palm near their table hid them from view, Anne unconsciously wrinkled her nose. The man was Kirt Callen and the girl with him looked practically young enough to be his daughter.

Apparently noticing her interest in something, Ty glanced back over his shoulder in the direction in which she was staring. The barest hint of a smile tugged at the corners of his mouth as he turned back to her. "I get the distinct impression that you dislike Kirt."

"You're right. I don't like him," she answered candidly, then lifted her hand in an uncertain gesture. "But I suppose I shouldn't say that to you. If you're his friend . . ."

"Frankly, I don't count Kirt as a friend," Ty said flatly. "He's a client, and we have mutual acquaintances, but that's about the extent of our relationship."

"I wonder why he leads such a shallow life," Anne mused. "There must be something better for him to do than chase after women."

"I guess he just doesn't choose to do anything better," Ty answered. Then he grinned as he looked at her. "But I suppose you'd rather believe he had a very unhappy childhood and that's why he lives the way he does now. Maybe if you had been able to go to medical school, you would have pursued a career in psychiatry. I've noticed that about you—you watch people. You were very interested in Jenny this past weekend."

"She seems so vulnerable." Toying with her napkin,

Anne looked at Ty directly. "That's why I was worried about Mr. Callen's obvious interest in her. She might not be able to see what kind of man he really is."

"Fortunately, she probably won't be seeing him at all anytime soon. I don't see him that often myself," Ty replied softly, his gaze narrowing as he leaned forward slightly, his arms resting on the table. "But I appreciate your concern for Jenny. Maybe you identify her with your own younger sisters."

"Probably," Anne confessed, smiling. "And I must admit that Sue and Amy—they're my sisters—have accused me more than once of trying to mother them too much. I recall being quite a tyrant when I was ten or so and Sue was five and Amy only two."

Though Ty smiled, he eyed her speculatively, then shook his head. "I simply can't see you as a tyrant, Anne. Gently persuasive, perhaps, but never a tyrant."

"A very chivalrous thing to say, Mr. Manning, but I assure you I can have quite a temper," Anne replied wryly. "You just don't know me."

"Ah, but I have every intention of changing that," he promised softly.

For an instant, Anne's heart stopped as she imagined there had been some hidden message in what he had said. Then she managed to convince herself that he was only trying to make up for his harsh words that morning and hadn't meant anything at all provocative by his statement. She smiled politely at him, but just as he started to speak again, he was interrupted by the waiter with their lunch. As they ate, the conversation remained lively, though less personal. Anne learned that he read a great deal, as she did, so there were never any periods of uncomfortable silence when neither of them could think of anything to say. One topic of conversation led to another, then another, including global politics, their favorite literature and even recent astonishing advances in the field of medicine, which was a subject that, of course, intrigued Anne.

By the time she had finished the delicious fillet of sole, Anne was beginning to realize that Ty was probably the most interesting man she had ever met. Knowledgeable in many subjects, he was never boring and he certainly wasn't the type of businessman who could only think in terms of profits and losses. And he could laugh at himself, a trait she found particularly appealing. As she refolded her napkin and tucked it beneath the edge of her plate, Anne smiled to herself when Ty asked the waiter, obviously a longtime acquaintance, about his family. He obviously had a genuine interest in people and that indicated a depth of character that rather surprised Anne. Because she knew there were many young women in his life, practically a different one every night, she had expected him to be a shallow person. Clearly, nothing could have been further from the truth. In less than three weeks she had seen so many different facets of his personality that now she was somewhat confused about how to react to him.

Deciding she would simply try to act naturally and hoping that would suffice, Anne smiled at Ty as the waiter left them alone again. Ty, however, was looking beyond her, his expression questioning. Suddenly, a hand descended on Anne's shoulder. She turned around and looked up, astonished to find that the hand belonged to her sister.

"Sue, what on earth?" she exclaimed softly, noticing the younger girl's flushed cheeks and wind-tousled hair. "What are you doing here? How did you get here from Washington? And why aren't you there in class? Is something wrong? You haven't heard from Mom? There's nothing wrong at home, is there?"

"No, nothing." Sue answered breathlessly, trying to

smooth her blond hair. "I took the bus from Washington because I had to see you. I really do have to talk to you right now, Anne. It's important."

Breathing a sigh of relief because nothing was wrong at home, Anne became quite calm again, knowing Sue had a tendency to exaggerage the importance of almost everything. Giving Ty an apologetic smile, she gestured toward an empty chair at the table. "Well, sit down. Mr. Manning, this is my sister, Sue. Sue, Mr. Manning."

"I don't want to sit down," Sue responded urgently, unable to stand still. "We have to talk right this minute, Anne. I mean it. It's very, very important."

Anne doubted that, but seeing how upset her sister was, she sighed resignedly and rose from her chair. "I'm sorry, Mr. Manning, but could you excuse me for a few minutes? I won't be long."

"Take your time," Ty said, giving her an understanding smile.

She led the way into the luxuriously appointed entrance foyer of the restaurant, but when she stopped beyond the coat-check desk, she was acting in such an agitated manner that Anne was becoming a bit concerned. "What is it, Sue? What's the matter?"

"Everything," the younger girl groaned melodramatically, then blurted out, "Oh, I might as well just tell you—I'm going to have to drop out of school!"

"You're most certainly not going to drop out of school," Anne responded emphatically, a no-nonsense gleam sparkling in her gray eyes. "What kind of silliness is this? What's made you decide you have to drop out? I've never heard anything so ridiculous. You just started college in January."

"What difference does that make?" Sue exclaimed, hands all aflutter. "Now that I know I won't be able to afford to go back next fall, what's the point of finishing this semester? I may as well just quit now and get a job."

Anne placed her hands on her hips. "What *are* you jabbering about? Why don't you think you'll be able to go back to college in the fall?"

"Because the price of tuition is going up! Everything's going up! We just won't be able to afford it." Sue twisted her hands together in front of her. "Yesterday, when I heard about the tuition, I thought maybe we could work something out. I tried to call you this morning, but you'd already left for work. So after my English class, I caught a bus and came here. I went to your office and the receptionist told me you were at this restaurant."

"Oh, Sue, I can hardly believe you came all this way just because your tuition costs will be rising next year. I expected them to. Didn't you?" Anne asked, striving not to lose her patience. Shaking her head, she smiled at her younger sister. "You're really getting all upset about nothing. I'm not upset, am I? I would be if I thought you wouldn't be able to go back to college next fall, but I know you will. You have nothing to worry about. I'll take care of everything. I'll work something out. Just put all this out of your mind and go back to school where you belong. This is my problem, and I'll take care of it, I promise you. You won't have to drop out of school."

"But . . . Anne, I don't want you to have to take care of it! You shouldn't have to."

"I don't have to. I want to."

Sue took a deep, shuddering breath. "You just don't understand. I wanted to go to college, and I enjoy it now that I'm there. But I'm not sure it's worth it, if you and Mom have to worry about money all the time just to keep me there. Sometimes I think I'd rather just quit and get a job."

"You're really not thinking straight." Touching a strand of her sister's hair, Anne shook her head. "What kind of job would you get?"

"One like yours, or at least eventually I could have one like yours. It's a good job, isn't it? You like it?"

"Yes," Anne said, glancing over her shoulder into the dining room. "And if I want to keep my good job, I'd better get back to Mr. Manning. He might not appreciate sitting there and waiting for me to finish talking about personal matters." She smiled at Sue. "Look, you just go back to Washington and try to make your afternoon classes. I'll call you at your dorm tonight and we'll talk some more. But I want you to put that idea about dropping out of school right out of your head. Okay?"

"But, Anne, I . . ."

"I really have to go now, honey," Anne insisted, brushing a kiss against Sue's still-flushed cheek. "Call you tonight." Then she hurried away before the younger girl could voice any more arguments. Idly twirling the wayward strand of hair at her temple, Anne walked back through the dining room, stiffening her shoulders as she felt the weight of another responsibility settle on them. So, Sue's tuition was going to cost more next year. And to add insult to injury, her car had picked this time to stop running. She would work out a solution though, she told herself firmly as she approached the table where Ty sat waiting. She had promised Sue she would be back in college next fall, and she had meant it.

"I'm terribly sorry, Mr. Manning," she said as she sat down across from him again and folded her hands on the tabletop. "I didn't mean to be gone so long."

"You weren't. Nothing's wrong, I hope?" His piercing blue eyes impaled hers. "Your sister seemed very upset."

"Oh, you know how it is when you're eighteen. Every problem seems insurmountable." Anne smiled, unaware that she did so rather wearily. "Sue just allowed herself to get upset over a minor problem that I'm sure I'll be able to handle."

For a long time, Ty said nothing. He simply watched her intently, his eyelids lowering slightly as if he were searching for something in the delicate features of her face. At last, he bowed his head. "We should be getting back to the office," he announced abruptly. "There are several appointments scheduled for this afternoon, I believe."

Nodding, Anne waited until he got up and came around to pull out her chair. She couldn't help regretting that it was back to business as usual. The lunch they had shared had been companionable, enjoyable . . . at least, it had been until Sue burst upon the scene, bearing news of yet another problem to solve. Trying to push all those minor personal troubles to the back of her mind, Anne preceded Ty into the foyer. There they were stopped by the maitre d', who handed Ty a folded scrap of lined paper. He opened it, glanced at Anne, then tucked the note into the breast pocket of his coat. Taking her elbow, he escorted her to the door. "Why don't you go back to the office? I'll be there in time for my first appointment." He patted the pocket that contained the note. "An acquaintance of mine wants to talk to me for a few minutes."

A beautiful woman acquaintance, no doubt, Anne thought as she left him. Twenty minutes later, as Anne was sorting the afternoon mail in the office, the telephone rang. It was the mechanic from the service station.

Anne took a deep breath. "Well, what's the verdict?"

"It's like this, miss," he answered, his tone distinctly

apologetic. "Just about everything's wrong with that old car of yours. First off, you got a cracked intake manifold. I could fix that for about $300. But there's so much else that needs fixing, too. I did a compression test and found out the rings are bad, and if you do the rings, miss, you ought to grind the valves. I'd probably have to replace the crankshaft and cam shaft bearings also."

"Whoa! All that sounds very expensive," Anne said. "How much do you think it would cost to fix everything?" When he told her, she sank back in her chair with a soft gasp. *"That much?"*

"Overhauls cost plenty these days, miss. Fifteen hundred dollars is about average. If I was you, I'd just junk this old car and buy me a new one. I know a junkyard dealer who'd probably give you $200 for her to get the parts. You interested?"

Actually, Anne was stunned. That old car had been part of her life for the past four years. But now it was being written off as a total wreck, and she was going to miss it. Yet she couldn't possibly pay $1500 to get it fixed. Nor could she buy a new car. Well, she would worry about that later. "I . . . I guess I might as well sell it," she said at last. "Could you ask the junkyard dealer if he'd like to buy it?"

"Sure can, miss. Talk to him tonight, most likely. Then I'll call you back tomorrow and tell you what he says."

When the conversation had concluded and Anne had replaced the receiver, she shook her head disbelievingly. "Why does everything always have to happen at once?" she muttered to herself, then went back to sorting the mail. A few minutes later when Ty buzzed her on the intercom, she was startled by the unexpected sound, because she hadn't realized he was back in his office yet. Usually, he entered his office through hers, but today he had obviously returned by the corridor entrance. When she answered the buzz and was told he wanted to see her, she automatically smoothed her skirt and went in.

She stopped short, however, the moment she stepped through the open doorway. Sue was sitting in the chair before Ty's desk! Anne's eyes darted to where he sat on the edge of the desk, legs outstretched in front of him. She met the enigmatic look in his gaze for an instant, then turned back to her sister. Why was Sue here? Before Anne could voice that question, Ty spoke.

"Come in, Anne. Close the doors," he commanded gently. "I called you in because I thought you should know Sue has just asked me for a job here at Manning Consultants."

Anne stared at her sister in sheer exasperation. When she spoke, however, she managed to sound calm. "Sue, why did you do that? I told you I'd take care of everything."

"I know what you told me," Sue answered, thrusting out her chin defiantly. "But I'm tired of having to worry about money. I'm tired of your having to. I'd rather quit school and go to work than have you go through all this hassle all the time."

"But it's worth it to me," Anne explained wearily. "I don't mind."

"But I do mind!" argued Sue, looking up at Ty as if to include him in the discussion. "I told Mr. Manning about the higher tuition, and I asked him for a job because I think it's time I gave up this useless dream of going to college."

"It isn't useless," Anne said tersely. "And you shouldn't have bored Mr. Manning with our little problems. He's a busy man."

"I know that," Sue replied stiffly, clenching the arms

of her chair. "I'm not a child, Anne. I hated to bother Mr. Manning, but I didn't know what else to do. You won't listen to me, so I thought if I could get him to hire me before you knew anything about it . . ."

"He isn't going to hire you, because you're not getting a job. You're going back to school and that's that. And stop thinking about money. That's for me to worry about."

"You're not my boss, Anne! I'm not a baby!" Sue cried, pursing her lips into a childish pout that seemed to belie her words. With a toss of her head, she turned to Ty. "Well, how about it, Mr. Manning? Will you give me a job as a file clerk or something?"

Stroking his jaw thoughtfully, he looked down at her, then up at Anne, his eyes narrowing as he seemed to detect the mute appeal in Anne's face. He glanced back down at Sue. "Tell me, do you enjoy college? Did you want to go, or did Anne insist that you go?"

Both girls were taken aback by the question, but Sue finally had to reluctantly admit, "Well, I wanted to go and I do enjoy it. But if you don't have enough money, you can't do everything you want to do."

Ty nodded. "I understand that, but I have to agree with Anne. Since you've started this semester, you should finish it. I think you should give her a chance to work out the financial problems. So I have to say no, Sue. I won't give you a job here. I think you might always regret it if I did."

"Big help you are," Sue muttered petulantly but remembered her manners when she stood up in front of him. "I shouldn't have said that. You have been very nice, and I appreciate your taking the time to talk to me. I shouldn't have bothered you, I know. Anne's right. You're busy, so I'm going now."

Anne followed her younger sister to the door that opened onto the corridor. For a moment they simply looked at each other, then Anne raised her eyes heavenward in mock exasperation.

"You've always been the peskiest little sister," she teased. "And you must be the most stubborn human being alive."

"After you, you mean," Sue retorted, but she smiled too, then shrugged. "All right, Anne, you win this round. I'll finish this semester. Then we'll see what happens."

With that temporary truce, they hugged briefly. After Sue had gone out the door, Anne squared her shoulders and turned to face Ty. "I'm awfully sorry she dragged you into this. I suppose the note you were given at the restaurant was from her? I should have recognized her stationery—torn-out notebook paper."

Smiling, Ty walked across the room to her. Tilting her chin up with one lean finger, he made her look at him. His smile faded. "Why do you do it? There are government loans."

She shrugged slightly. "Mom and I just didn't want her to have to face a big debt like that after she graduated. Besides, I don't mind helping her. It just won't be as easy now that the costs are going up . . . again. But that's a problem Sue shouldn't have gotten all upset about. And she certainly shouldn't have bothered you with it."

"It was no bother, Anne. I'm glad I know what you're doing," Ty said, laying both his hands on her shoulders. "Maybe I can help. No, don't go all tense as though I've insulted you. I'm not going to offer you a donation for the college fund, but I am going to give you a raise."

"You are not! I won't take it!" A foreboding silence filled the room after the last word was said, and scarlet color tinted Anne's cheeks as she realized that was not exactly the best way for a secretary to talk to her boss.

She gestured nervously. "What I mean is I don't expect you to give me a raise simply because you know I need more money for Sue."

As Ty gazed down at her, his fingers began an evocative brushing motion over the sensitive, satiny skin of her neck. "You're an excellent secretary, Anne," he said, his voice low and somehow almost seductive. "And since I planned to give you a raise in a couple of months anyway, I don't see how you can object to getting one now."

"But I do object," she murmured, trying to ignore the disruptive effect his caressing touch was having on her senses. She flexed her shoulders slightly, hoping he would remove his hands, but when he didn't, she tried to relax. Clasping her hands behind her back, she attempted to explain her feelings. "Look, I just don't want you to think you *should* give me special consideration because you know I could use extra money. I would be uncomfortable getting a raise that way. I want to earn any I ever get."

"Anne, don't be so obstinate," he said softly, coaxingly, his hands cupping her face. "Most secretaries don't make as much money as they deserve, considering all they do. So you might say you've already earned a raise. Now, just accept it."

"I will . . . in a couple of months, since that's when you'd planned to give me one," she answered weakly, wishing she wasn't so aware of his nearness. "Until then, I'll make do with my present salary."

"Don't try to be so independent, Anne. You deserve the raise and you need the money. Just take it."

Anne bit down on her lower lip, and her expression was momentarily uncertain as she looked up at him. For a fleeeting instant, his offer was a temptation. He had so much money, and sometimes she did get so tired of having to worry about every penny. Yet . . . she couldn't take what would really be charity. At last she shook her head. "I appreciate your offer, really I do, but I can't accept it."

"You mean you won't," he countered, his fingers feathering over the rapidly beating pulse in her throat. "Anne, stop trying to be so tough and self-sufficient. We all should know how to take as well as give. And I think you give too much to your family. It's time you learned to take something out of life for yourself. Maybe you should start learning right now."

Before she could react, his thumbs tilted her face up as he lowered his dark head. She took a swift, startled breath as his mouth descended to move slowly over her own. She tensed. Her hands came up to tightly clutch his lapels.

"Relax," he whispered coaxingly, slipping one arm down around her slim waist to draw her firmly against him. "You do have needs of your own, Anne. Stop trying to deny them."

It was impossible to deny what she needed right now: the desire to remain close to him was nearly overpowering in intensity. His warmth and the fresh masculine scent of his skin enveloped her. Their bodies seemed to fit together perfectly, the soft contours of hers yielding to the firmer line of his. His lips trailed over her cheek and along the smooth line of her jaw, igniting a fire that surged through her veins, inflaming her senses. When his mouth covered hers again, she was powerless to prevent her lips from parting to the probing tip of his tongue. With her involuntary response, his kiss deepened, became an intimate exploration. Every inch of her skin seemed sensitized to the touch of the lean hands that slipped beneath her suit jacked to move over her back. Her fingers loosened their grip on his lapels to spread open against his shirtfront as her lips clung to his.

When at last he held her slightly away from him, her eyes fluttered open to meet the passionate glimmer in his. She blushed and he smiled indulgently.

"You see, Anne, you do have needs, don't you?" he asked softly, his hands moving down to span her waist. "You must have if you could allow yourself to break that old rule about never kissing the boss."

He was gently teasing her, but she was so disturbed by her ardent response that she murmured defensively, "I didn't break the rule. *You* kissed *me*."

"But you kissed back," he whispered, and before she could reply, his mouth took hers again.

This time his kiss was electrifying, and caution and inhibitions were overwhelmed by the need to surrender to the desires he aroused in her. All resistance ebbed. She stretched up on tiptoe. Her arms slipped around his neck. As the soft curves of her breasts yielded to his muscular chest and he gathered her closer, a central throbbing ache awakened within her, then radiated throughout her body. Her mouth opened slightly as his lips hardened and became increasingly demanding, parting the soft shape of hers with a taking pressure she couldn't resist. She did kiss him back, somewhat hesitantly, and though he was the aggressor, she was undeniably responsive. She delighted in his strength and found a warm satisfying joy in the arms tightening around her as if they couldn't hold her close enough. His warm minty breath caressed her mouth, then his teeth nipped gently on the full curve of her lower lip, sending a thrill of sensual excitement pulsating through her. She moaned softly, but as his hands slid around to cup the sides of her breasts, his palms pressing down evocatively into the firm, cushiony flesh, the forbidden caress shocked her back to reality.

"Ty, no," she protested softly, then broke away from him and hurried toward the door.

"Anne, why are you being so obstinate?" he called after her, before she could escape. When she turned reluctantly to look back at him, he regarded her with solemn intensity. "Couldn't you let me help you with Sue's expenses?"

"No. You're very kind to offer, but I think it would be a bad idea." Feeling she owed him some reasonable explanation, she breathed a sigh. "I . . . want to keep our relationship strictly professional."

"You've told me that," he persisted. "Now, tell me why."

"I, well, I made a mistake once, and that's enough. I got a little too involved with my first employer, but he wasn't seriously interested in me. It was a painful, embarrassing situation, so finally I quit my job and came to work here. And I . . . never want to have to disrupt my life that way again. I promised myself then, I'd never get involved with my superiors."

"Really?" Ty countered, compressing his lips into a grim line. "Then I suppose that means you won't be seeing Mike Bennett again socially, will you?"

Anne simply stared at him, unable to tell him that Mike was different. He was a friend and certainly posed no potential threat to her happiness. But Ty did. Whenever he touched her, she felt as if he controlled her completely. Deep inside, she was afraid he might become too important in her life if she let him. Yet she couldn't admit that, so she murmured instead, "Mike's not my boss, so I don't see how any of this applies to him."

"How convenient. But I see how it applies. Technically, Mike is your superior. He has an executive position in this company, and I think you'd be wise to stop seeing him . . . if you want to be consistent in obeying your own self-imposed rules."

"Are you forbidding me to go out with Mike?" Anne

asked heatedly, incensed once again by his autocratic tone. "Is that what you're saying?"

"I'm not your keeper, Anne," he answered, shrugging indifferently. "Do as you please. Just remember that hypocrisy isn't an endearing quality."

Hypocrisy! Drawing herself up to her full height, Anne had to fight back the angry retort that trembled on her lips. He dared call *her* a hypocrite! And he was trying to engage her in a casual involvement, while at the same time he was having an affair with Millicent Beaumont! Anne longed to hurl that pithy reminder at him, but innate common sense told her that would be a superb way to get herself fired. Gritting her teeth instead, she turned on one heel and rushed out of the room without looking back. After closing the doors behind her, she stood in her own office, trembling and angry at herself. Every time Ty touched her, and especially when he kissed her, she responded like an ardent little fool, and she simply couldn't continue to react like that. She couldn't, because if she did, intuition told her that she would live to bitterly regret it.

Chapter Five

Within two weeks spring had transformed Alexandria. Scarlet tulips and yellow daffodils nodded in the gentle breezes, and tiny, nearly transparent green leaves appeared on the trees. Unfortunately, Anne didn't have a great deal of time to enjoy the beauty of this new spring because she had taken a second job. Without a car, she had no way to commute to the dress shop, so she had applied for a job as a waitress in a restaurant within walking distance of her apartment. Because she had been a waitress during summers while in high school, she was able to accustom herself to the restaurant's routine very quickly. Luckily, her fellow employees were very pleasant, so it was a good second job. Best of all, because the Colonial was the best restaurant in town, and, therefore, outrageously expensive, she received generous tips. But the hours were long, and she often didn't get home until nearly midnight. By that time, she was nearly exhausted and usually bathed and fell into bed as quickly as she possibly could.

Working so many hours each day wasn't terrific fun, but it was imperative that she save money to cover the higher cost of Sue's college expenses next fall. After the first semester was paid for, she hoped she could find some less tiring solution to her financial problems. In the meantime, she felt she was lucky to have found a second job that paid so well, at least in tips.

One Thursday evening she rushed home from the office to press the simple, but rather classy, uniform she wore at the restaurant. Black, with a straight skirt and scoop neckline, it had white georgette sleeves and apron and complemented her fair hair and creamy complexion. After the ironing was done, she hung the uniform on a hanger and covered it with plastic. She glanced at the clock on the kitchen wall. There was just enough time for her to redo her hair before leaving for work.

Three hours later, Anne's energy was beginning to flag. She had just finished serving a party of twelve, no easy task even when the patrons were exceedingly nice, and these people hadn't been exceedingly nice. They had made her job difficult from the beginning, three of them changing their minds about what they wanted to eat just when she had been about to bring their original orders out from the kitchen. Then, two of the women had complained that their steaks weren't rare enough, glaring at Anne as if she had cooked them herself. Yet Anne had been gracious and pleasant through it all and had finally managed to satisfy them, temporarily anyway. Pausing for a moment to give her feet a rest in the hallway between the kitchen and the elegant dining room, she leaned her head against the wall but straightened immediately when the door from the dining room swung open. Pat Martin, a young mother of two who worked at the restaurant to supplement her husband's income, came marching down the hall, stopped before Anne and perched her hands on her hips.

"Some people are really the limit," she proclaimed, shaking her head. "You remember that hoity-toity senator and his wife at table eight? Well, their check totaled eighty dollars, and they kept me running back and forth to their table every minute they were here. But would you believe they only left me a three-dollar tip?"

"Remember now, smile and the world smiles with you," Anne said wryly, patting the older woman's shoulder sympathetically. "Now, if only we could get it to work that way all the time. We smile, but sometimes they don't smile back." Pat growled softly to ease her frustration, as Anne smiled and stepped past her. "Well, I'd better get back before Andre comes looking for me."

Leaving Pat in the hallway sliding her feet in and out of her shoes, Anne stepped back into the dimly lighted dining room just in time to catch the maitre d's eye. Andre, a tall, dignified man who was amazingly friendly, unobstrusively held up four fingers, then two. Anne nodded and, taking two gold-embossed menus, proceeded to table four near the far back corner. In the most private area of the room, the table was usually reserved for frequent patrons of the restaurant. Looking down to be certain her little white apron was straight, Anne approached the table. When she lifted her head, she wished she could have sunk right through the floor. Her polite smile froze on her lips, her cheeks felt stiff and her muscles tightened as she met Ty's startled stare. His surprise was mirrored in his eyes for only an instant, however, before they turned an icy blue and narrowed dangerously. Detecting the grim tightening of his jaw, she fumbled in her pocket for her pencil, then realized he and his apparently constant companion, Millicent Beaumont, hadn't even looked at the menus yet. She gave the woman one, then handed Ty his warily, half expecting him to jerk it out of her hand. But he didn't. He simply looked at her.

She gulped. "Good evening, Mr. Manning," she said, her voice embarrassingly squeaky as she surreptitiously brushed her suddenly damp palms over her apron. "Could I get you a drink while the two of you are deciding?"

"What would you like, Millicent?" he asked his date brusquely, then glanced back up at Anne after Millicent decided on an aperitif. "And I'll have a Scotch and water."

His low tone was so cold and unfriendly that even Millicent apparently sensed all was not right. Her curious gaze drifted from his lean tanned face to Anne's much paler one, which she had not even glanced at until then. A rather perverse amusement curled her glossed lips as she recognized the other girl, and she didn't seem at all surprised to find Anne working at yet another dull, commonplace job.

"I'll get your drinks," Anne murmured. She walked away sedately, though she had to fight the urge to run across the dining room to the bar. When she had told Henry the bartender what she wanted, she stood waiting, staring off into space.

"What's the matter with you?" Pat exclaimed softly, stepping in front of Anne. "You look like you've seen a ghost. You're so pale."

"Not a ghost. Just my boss," Anne told her, tugging at the wayward tendril of her hair. "And he didn't know I had a second job. I guess I should have told him, but I didn't think he'd care much for the idea. And, judging by the way he just looked at me, I could be in a lot of trouble."

"So? If he says anything to you, tell him you wouldn't have to hold down two jobs, if he'd pay you enough money," Pat advised. "That's what I'd do."

Anne smiled wanly, unwilling to admit that Ty had offered her a raise and she had refused it. That would be too complicated to explain, so she said nothing. Then Henry placed the two drinks on a tray on the bar. Squaring her shoulders resolutely, Anne picked up the tray and walked back to Ty's table.

The evening lasted forever. Every time he spoke, Ty's voice possessed that cold, hard edge that she knew meant he was very displeased. She thought he and Millicent would never leave the restaurant, yet when they did finally go, she felt worse still. Considering the way Millicent clung to his arm and gazed adoringly up at him, Anne could only imagine that their evening together wouldn't be ending very soon. And she found that thought almost as distressing as the fact that she would have to face Ty's displeasure the next morning, which was only a few short hours away.

Anne was at her desk Friday morning when Ty strode in. His early arrival caught her by surprise. He, too, seemed surprised to find her there, and when he regarded her intently for several seconds, then glanced at his wristwatch, dread dragged at her stomach.

"Why are you here already?" he asked flatly, his expression unreadable. "You're almost an hour early."

"I've been taking the early bus in," she explained without really meeting his narrowed gaze. "If I took the next bus, I'd get here with only five minutes to spare, and I like to have more time than that to prepare for the day."

"And why are you taking the bus in the first place? Didn't you tell me you have a car?"

"Did have. I had to junk it," she answered with a resigned shrug of her shoulders. Briefly explaining what had happened, she finished, "The car was just too old to make a $1,500 repair bill worthwhile."

For some odd reason this information seemed to irritate Ty. Muttering incomprehensibly beneath his breath, he reached into the inside breast pocket of his light gray pinstriped suit jacket and brought out a business card. "I came in early to call Paris. But since you're here, would you mind putting the call through for me?"

"Of course not," she murmured, taking the card he handed her. Relief washed over her. This obviously important call had given her a temporary reprieve from the inevitable confrontation with him. And maybe if she was extremely lucky, she thought hopefully, he would even forget that he had seen her last night.

She wasn't that lucky. Her hopes died a swift death with Ty's next, curtly spoken words, "And after I've finished talking to Paris, I'll want to see you in my office. I think you know exactly what about."

So much for that short-lived reprieve, she told herself, heaving a worried sigh as Ty strode into his own office and closed the doors behind him. Staring unseeingly at the business card she held, she could only hope Ty would try to be understanding when he had his little talk with her. Many employers didn't approve of their employees moonlighting, and apparently Ty was one who didn't. Yet since he knew why she had taken a second job, maybe he would take her special circumstances into consideration. Praying he would, Anne picked up the telephone receiver and proceeded to push the buttons for the seemingly endless string of numbers involved in the direct-dial overseas call.

In less than two minutes, she was connected with Francois Boulet in Paris, and after switching the call to Ty's office, she replaced the receiver in its cradle. Her hand was trembling slightly, and she berated herself for feeling so apprehensive. Ty, after all, was no ogre. In the weeks she had worked directly with him, he had proven himself to be a fair man where his employees were concerned. She had no reason to fear he would be unfair to her. Or did she?

With that unanswerable question buzzing around in her head, she wandered about her office for the next twenty minutes, trying to occupy her mind by doing mundane tasks. The effort was useless. Her eyes were drawn innumerable times to her phone, but the button for Ty's line was still alight, and she began to wish his call to Paris would end so the two of them could just go ahead and get the confrontation over and done with.

At last she forced herself to go back to her desk. It was when she was making a list of Ty's afternoon appointments that Jenny Manning strolled into the office.

"I have to see my brother," she announced loftily, strolling toward the double doors as if she meant to walk right in.

"Would you mind waiting out here, Miss Manning?" Anne suggested politely. "Mr. Manning's on the phone to Paris, but he should be finished soon. If you'll just wait . . ."

"Oh, all right," Jenny acquiesced, though not very graciously. Walking across the room, she stood staring out the tinted window.

Once again, Anne was aware of the girl's unhappiness, though Jenny tried to disguise it beneath that hard veneer of rebellious hostility. Try as she might to appear cold and unfeeling by making caustic remarks, she couldn't completely hide the pain and confusion that darkened her eyes and etched shallow lines of dissatisfaction in her young face. Anne pitied her and, ignoring her deliberate unfriendliness, decided to try to strike up a conversation.

"Mr. Manning told me you're in college in Washington," she began. "So is my sister, although she doesn't go to the same university you do. She lives on campus, but you commute from here everyday, don't you?"

The girl's only answer was a short affirmative noise from her throat, but Anne wasn't one to let surliness deter her. "Sue—that's my sister—is really happy in college. How about you? Do you enjoy going?"

"Not especially," Jenny mumbled, then spun around on one heel to glower at Anne. "Look, I don't have a lot of time to chitchat. Is Ty still on the phone, or can I go in to see him now? He's got to give me some extra spending money."

The deliberate rebuff didn't bother Anne unduly. She glanced down at her phone just as the light beneath the panel button went out, indicating that Ty's line was now open. She smiled up at Jenny. "He's just finished his call. Let me buzz him and tell him you're here."

"Never mind," Jenny said, with an imperious toss of her head. "I'll just go in. I don't think I have to be announced to my own brother."

As Jenny walked into Ty's office without first knocking, Anne shook her head regretfully. She was a lovely girl and it was such a shame she was too unhappy to allow her personality to match her physical attractiveness. Sullen teenagers had few friends, so Jenny was hurting herself more than anyone else by behaving so antagonistically. Wishing there was some way to help the girl, Anne went back to her list of Ty's appointments. It was only a few seconds later that the shouting started.

Jenny's voice, stridently angry, carried through the double doors. Though her words were incomprehensible, Anne shifted restlessly in her chair, feeling almost as if she were eavesdropping on a family spat that was none of her business. It was as though Jenny was having a shouting match with herself. Anne never heard Ty's voice at all, though she assumed he was speaking during the frequent lulls in Jenny's tirade. But, of course, Ty never raised his voice, even in moments of extreme provocation. Anne didn't really expect him to start yelling now.

He didn't disappoint her. When the battle in his office ended a short time later, and Jenny slammed open the doors on her way out, he still hadn't once raised his voice. At her desk Anne watched Jenny march swiftly across the room, her face an angry red. Then she jerked open the outer office door and banged it shut behind her.

As the girl's loud footsteps receded along the corridor, Ty buzzed Anne, startling her. Now it was her turn to face him, and she was quite sure Jenny's visit hadn't left him in a very good mood. Taking a deep, calming breath, she unnecessarily smoothed the skirt of her green jersey dress and walked through the open doorway into Ty's office.

Ty was standing by the window, looking out over the city, his hands in his pockets. He didn't turn around. "Well, you were right, Anne," he said abruptly. "I should have talked to Jenny about Kirt Callen. He didn't just forget about her, as I thought he would. He's been calling her, and I just discovered that she's very flattered by all his attention."

Anne grimaced. "She certainly doesn't need a man like him in her life right now. But I'm sure you just told her that, didn't you, and that's why she left here in such a huff?"

Nodding, Ty moved away from the window. Shedding his jacket, he tossed it onto a chair. "That was one reason she was upset, yes. She didn't appreciate my assessment of Kirt. She thinks he's, in her words, 'a super guy.'"

"If only she knew what a skirt chaser he is."

"But she doesn't know," Ty said grimly, loosening his tie. "In fact, she thinks he's so super she had lunch with him yesterday. Of course, she didn't tell me that. Mike Bennett saw her with Kirt and mentioned it to me this morning."

"Oh dear, I really hate to hear she's actually gone out with him," Anne murmured, genuinely concerned. "I guess it would be useless for you to forbid her to see him again?"

"Undoubtedly, but I have to admit I lost my temper and told her not to go out with him again anyway." Ty replied, a threatening glint appearing in his eyes. "Now I suppose my next step is to tell Kirt to leave her alone."

"I'm not sure he can leave any young girl alone. Maybe your best bet would be to get Jenny out of Alexandria and away from him altogether. Couldn't you take her on a small vacation, someplace where she can relax and have fun, get to know you a little better?"

Ty shook his head. "Unfortunately I'm too busy just now. I am going on a business trip to St. Croix, though, in a few weeks. The client, Bob Peterson, is an old friend of the family. Maybe Jenny could come along."

"That might help a lot. She needs to spend time with you. Doesn't she have anyone else she can talk to?"

"Not that I know of. Even before Mother went to Europe, she and Jenny weren't communicating at all. And I'm not sure that Jenny *wants* to spend time with me. She seems to have this particular resentment toward me."

"Probably because you took over here at Manning Consultants after your father died. She could resent you because she thinks you're trying to take his place," Anne conjectured gently. "And you do resemble him. That might upset her."

"That's a very real possibility, but I think she'll eventually get over feeling that way. She just needs time. So my immediate concern is keeping her away from Kirt, and I'm not sure how to accomplish that. Lecturing her won't help, and I can't watch her every minute. There are too many evenings when I have business meetings, and sometimes I have to be away overnight. That means she'll have opportunities to see Kirt, if she really wants to. I wish I could believe she'd recognize him for what he is, but as you said, she's very vulnerable right now."

As Ty wearily rubbed his hand over the back of his neck, Anne felt an unreasonable need to comfort him. Impulsively, she went to him and actually reached out as if to touch his arm before she realized she shouldn't and let her hand drop. "I know how upsetting this must be to you," she said softly. "I really wish I could do something to help."

Almost instantaneously, Ty's expression altered. Something akin to triumph gleamed in his eyes, and a half smile tugged at the corners of his firm, sensuously carved lips as he removed his hands from his pockets and folded his arms across his chest. "Of course," he murmured cryptically. "The answer's obvious."

"Answer?" Anne questioned bewilderedly. "I don't understand what you mean."

"It's very simple, Anne. You'll quit your job at the restaurant and move into my house, where you can keep an eye on Jenny in the evenings when I'm gone.

And as you said, she needs a friend. I think you could get close to her."

Anne could hardly believe she had heard him correctly. For several seconds she stared blankly at him, then shook her head slowly, as if reassembling her thoughts. "I . . . couldn't just move into your house, Mr. Manning. I . . ."

"Of course, I'd pay you more than you're making at the restaurant."

"But my apartment—I couldn't just give it up."

"I wouldn't expect you to," he replied flatly. "You'll keep your apartment, but you just won't live there until Jenny's lost interest in Kirt Callen. After she comes to her senses about him, you can go back."

Anne gestured helplessly, searching her brain for some convincing way to decline his offer without telling him the truth: that she would feel extremely uneasy living in the same house with him, considering the strong physical attraction that sometimes flared between them. Unwilling to embarrass herself by admitting that, she tried frantically to think of another plausible excuse and finally came up with one that was very sensible. "It wouldn't work, Mr. Manning. Jenny would know I was there to keep an eye on her, and she would resent me too much to ever want to be close to me."

"I trust your ability to get through to her," Ty countered, undaunted even by that argument. "You're young enough to relate to her, and since your father died when you were seventeen, too, you can understand some of what she's feeling right now. Can't you?"

"Well, yes, but . . ."

"Besides, I'll pay you enough to enable you to send more money to Sue," he said softly, his lean brown hands coming out to curve around her upper arms. "It would be a good arrangement for everybody, Anne, especially you. You can't go on working here all day and at the restaurant half the night. That's no kind of life."

Gazing up at him, Anne hesitated, necessity making her consider the fact that he was offering her a chance to send more money to Sue. Yet, with the added income of her second job, she was earning enough to keep her sister in college. She wasn't desperately in need of the extra money Ty was offering. And since the mere touch of his hands on her arms sent a shiver of sensual awareness along her spine, she knew it would be the height of folly to even contemplate living in the same house with him. Deciding it would be wiser to be safe than sorry, she finally shook her head. "I'd like to help Jenny, but I know she'd resent me. I don't think moving into your house would be a good idea. I'm sorry, but I can't do it."

"Anne, you're forgetting a very important detail," he said, his voice lowering. "You can't go on working here and at the restaurant, too."

"But it's not so bad, really," she protested, stretching the truth a bit. "I don't mind working in the evenings."

His narrowed gaze captured and held hers. "Maybe I didn't make myself clear," he said, his tone taking on that hard, ominous edge. "When I say you can't continue to work both here and at the restaurant, I mean I won't allow it. I don't tolerate moonlighting, Anne, except when dire circumstances warrant it. Your circumstances aren't dire. I offered you a raise, but you refused it. Now I'm offering to pay you to help me with Jenny, but you've refused that too. One way or the other, you'll have to quit your job as a waitress. You're my secretary, Anne, and I have to be able to depend on you. I can't if you're always tired. To put it bluntly, either you quit the job at the restaurant or I'll have to fire you."

"You don't mean that!" Anne gasped softly, her cheeks turning pale. "You wouldn't . . . couldn't be that unfair! How could you justify firing me when you have no reason to complain about my work? I do everything I'm supposed to do and I do it very well!"

"Do you, Anne?" he asked lazily, his fingers tightening their grip on her arms, his expression enigmatic. "Then tell me about those very important contracts you sent air express to Denver on Tuesday."

"*Oh no,*" she breathed, chagrin putting some color back into her cheeks. "I forgot to send them!"

"Yes, you did. And you didn't even realize you hadn't sent them until I reminded you just now. That's not like you, Anne."

She hardly heard him. "I don't even know where the contracts are, unless I filed them by mistake. But I'll find them right now, I promise you, and send them out immediately."

As she tried to pull away, Ty held her fast. "Never mind. They've been sent. After you left Tuesday evening, I found them on your desk and had Betsy send them air express."

"Why didn't you tell me that Wednesday morning?" Anne asked weakly. "You never said a word about it."

"There was no reason to. Everybody makes mistakes, and even though you make fewer than any secretary I've ever had, I didn't think much about your forgetting the contracts, until last night." Pausing, he surveyed her delicate features with solemn intensity. "But when I saw you slaving in that restaurant, I knew why you'd forgotten them. If you're exhausted, you can't expect to be efficient here."

Anne was mortified. Focusing her gaze on the pulse

that beat with fascinating regularity in his throat, she breathed a soft sigh. Never once in five years had anyone chastised her for not doing her work well, and it was a humiliating experience to have to admit to herself that Ty had just cause to chastise her now. She swallowed with difficulty. "I'm sorry about the contracts. Nothing like that will happen again. But . . ." The edge of her small white teeth pressed down on her lower lip. "But it was only one mistake. And I have to keep that job as a waitress so I can send Sue money. Couldn't you please reconsider?"

"No, Anne," he answered firmly, the set of his strong jaw implacable. "I won't reconsider. You can move in with Jenny and me and make more money for Sue than you're making now, or you can keep your job at the restaurant and lose this one. What's your decision?"

"You're not leaving me with much of a choice," she retorted, thrusting out her small chin rather defiantly. "Are you?"

"No choice at all, as far as I can see," he admitted tonelessly. "So it's settled. I want you to move into the house tomorrow night, because, as you know, I have that trip to San Francisco this weekend, and I don't want to leave Jenny alone."

"It's not going to work out, you know," Anne declared impetuously. "She's not going to be thrilled having me there, spying on her."

"I'm hoping you can become her friend, but if you can't, she'll just have to accept the arrangement anyhow." He shrugged. "She's my sister and she's acting very immaturely lately. I don't intend to leave her alone there so Kirt Callen can take advantage of her. You might be able to help her see him for what he is. I know you don't want him to have a chance to ruin her life."

"Of course I don't. I'd really like to help her, but . . ."

"You'll be helping yourself too, Anne," Ty interrupted gently, trailing one fingertip over the delicate skin beneath her eyes. "You look tired. I could have turned you over my knee when I saw you last night. You've been exhausting yourself, trying to hold down two jobs."

"Not really. I'm fine. I . . ."

"You've lost weight."

"No, I haven't."

"Yes, you have. I can tell," he murmured, his large hands dropping down to span her waist. "You're thinner than you were the last time I did this."

Anne's heart jumped. She wished he hadn't said that. Since that day he had kissed her and she had rushed out of his office, she had tried to maintain a cool, strictly professional relationship with him. She had only partially succeeded. Though he had never given any indication that he wanted to repeat that episode, she hadn't been able to completely forget how his kiss had made her feel. And right now, the touch of his hands on her narrow waist wasn't helping her achieve forgetfulness. Her wide gray eyes sought his as she shifted her feet self-consciously. "There'll be gossip, you know," she murmured, saying the first thing that came into her mind. "If I move into your house, people will think . . . that we . . ."

"Maybe they'll be right," he whispered provocatively, tracing the soft shape of her mouth with one fingertip. And when her lips parted with a swift intake of breath, he lowered his head.

Unable to move, almost mesmerized by the enticing look in his dark blue eyes, she could only murmur a soft protest before his mouth descended on hers. Then it was too late. Her own eyes fluttered shut, and she was swept up in dizzying sensations too delightful to resist, as his hard marauding lips moved against hers. Every inch of her skin caught fire, and her breath caught in her throat as his hands came up to cup her breasts. His fingers curved into the cushioned softness, his thumbs moving caressingly over the suddenly aching peaks, until they surged tautly beneath his touch.

His gently exploring fingers were warm through the thin fabric of her blouse and brief lace bra. Anne's legs weakened as he drew her closer against him. Her arms encircled his neck and her fingers tangled in the thick clean hair on his nape. She relaxed against him, all pliant feminine warmth. Delighting in the firm, seeking lips that plundered hers, she kissed him back with an urgency that almost equaled his. Yet, when his hands moved down her back to cover her gently curving hips and he molded her body to his, forcing her awareness of his desire, she tensed, her pulses pounding.

"Ty, no," she breathed, turning her mouth away from his. As her hands slipped down to press against his chest, she could feel the rapid beating of his heart. Her body, still burning from his caresses, urged her to go back into his arms, but her brain urged caution. She took a jerky step backward, away from him. Unable to look at him directly, she touched trembling fingers to one temple. "This . . . sort of thing isn't . . . part of the arrangement, is it?"

"It could be," he answered, his voice appealingly husky. "But only if you want it to be."

"I don't," she said hastily, but somehow the words sounded ridiculously unconvincing, even to her, and rosy color suffused her cheeks. With a muffled exclamation, she spun around and started to rush away. She was stopped as Ty reached after her and caught her arm.

He turned her to him. One lean finger tipped up her

chin, so she had to look at him as his dark gaze drifted over her, lingering on her still-parted lips before moving up to meet her eyes. "Don't be afraid of me, Anne," he commanded softly. "You have no reason to be. I'm not one of those men who finds fear in a woman exhilarating. So I don't want fear from you."

"What *do* you want?" she asked tremulously. And when a flame flickered in his eyes and answered her question quite clearly, she turned and made her escape from the room, wondering just how she was going to handle him now. Here in the office, she was able to remind herself constantly that he was her employer and that she couldn't become involved with him. Yet such self-assurance might not be very convincing, once she was living with him in the same house.

Chapter Six

It was Sunday night. In the study of the Manning house, Anne closed the book she was reading and, crossing her arms behind her head, stretched lazily. She lowered her feet, which she had tucked up beside her in the chair, and slid them into her favorite, rather worn, canvas espadrilles. Standing, she stretched again and smiled slightly. For the first time in over two weeks, she felt thoroughly relaxed and well-rested. Due to the two full nights' sleep she had gotten since moving into the house on Friday, she no longer felt as if she were running on sheer nervous energy.

She was almost relieved that Ty had practically blackmailed her into coming to stay in his house, though she still questioned his method of achieving what he wanted. It hadn't been particularly fair of him to threaten to fire her simply because she had made the mistake of forgetting to send those contracts to Denver. On the other hand, Anne couldn't really blame him for taking advantage of her mistake, so he could compel her to move in and keep an eye on his sister. In fact, she had to admire him for the concern he felt for Jenny. Some businessmen were so involved with their work that they were fairly oblivious to the feelings of the people they should be closest to. At least Ty recognized the fact that at the moment Jenny was very confused and very vulnerable. So Anne really couldn't fault him very much for doing everything in his power to protect his younger sister.

Tugging the bottom of her peach cotton-knit sweater down over her slim hips, Anne glanced around the comfortably furnished study. Books lined two walls from floor to ceiling. A large globe on a carved wooden stand sat beside a mammoth oak desk. Small tables were at each end of the brown leather sofa and beside each of two matching chairs. It was a cozy room, conducive to quiet contemplation, and Anne suspected Ty probably spent a good deal of his time in here. She couldn't know that for sure, however, since he had left for San Francisco on Friday, shortly after she had moved into the house, and wasn't due back until later tonight. In a way, she dreaded his return. His absence during the weekend had enabled her to adapt to her new surroundings without the added pressure of having to cope with him.

Unfortunately, becoming accustomed to the Manning home was all she had accomplished in the past few days. Though she had hoped to begin getting acquainted with Jenny, the younger girl hadn't cooperated. Jenny had stayed in her room almost continuously since Friday, much to Anne's surprise. At least that meant the girl wasn't with Kirt Callen, though Anne suspected she had talked to him on the phone several times. It had distressed Anne to take all her meals alone in the elegant dining room, while Jenny had hers on a tray up in her room, but she had respected the girl's desire to be by herself. If she was to have any sort of relationship with Ty's sister, she knew she would need to proceed slowly or risk alienating Jenny altogether. Still, Anne knew she herself would have to make the first friendly overtures.

Thoughtfully tugging at the tendril of hair that grazed her cheek, she stared out across the room for a moment or so, then decided it wasn't too soon to pay Jenny a casual visit in her room. After picking up her book, she left the study and walked across the wide entrance hall to the curving polished stairs. As she placed a foot on the first step, she paused a moment to admire the rich patina of the gleaming hardwood floor. It was buffed to such a high gloss that it reflected the light from the crystal chandelier suspended from the ceiling.

The Manning house appealed to Anne. Constructed in the mid-1800's, it was situated a few miles south of Alexandria and sat on a gently sloping hill, lushly green with grass and scattered with huge old oak trees. And the interior of the house was every bit as impressive as the exterior. The grand hall ran from front to back and opened on to a large drawing room, a smaller sitting room and a spacious dining room, as well as the study. It was a lovely old home, but Anne felt rather lonely in it. She supposed that would change when Ty returned and Jenny finally decided to stop hiding in her room.

As Anne reached the head of the stairs, her shoes sank down in the thick pile of a sculptured beige carpet. She admired the Oriental silk screen that decorated the left wall of the wide corridor. Outside Jenny's room, she listened for some signs of activity within, but heard nothing. Although she wasn't sure what she was going to say to Jenny, she knocked, then opened the door upon hearing a fairly unenthusiastic invitation to enter.

For Anne's tastes, Jenny's room was too frilly by far.

Featuring a bed with a white organdy canopy, windows with ruffled organdy curtains and a dark pink carpet, it seemed appropriate for a much younger girl. Shelves built into one wall were laden with countless expensive stuffed animals that looked far too clean and well-preserved to have ever been cuddled or dragged around by one ear by a little girl who loved them. Jenny lay sprawled on her stomach on the ruffled organdy coverlet atop her bed, looking as out of place as a bull in a china shop in her patched jeans and bedraggled sweatshirt.

Her chin cupped in her hands, she looked up from the papers scattered on the bed before her. As she gazed at Anne, her eyes were as aloofly cool as Ty's could sometimes be, and her only visible reaction to the intrusion was a slightly haughty uplifting of her dark, nicely arched brows.

"I got tired of reading and was feeling a little lonely," Anne began honestly, giving the younger girl a smile. "I thought maybe we could talk for awhile. Or are you busy?"

Jenny sniffed. "I was just going over my notes for a history term paper, but they're boring me to tears. What the devil do I care about the First World War?" Her blue eyes glittered challengingly. "Maybe I'll just forget the whole thing and not turn in a paper at all."

"That's always an option, I guess," Anne responded with an unconcerned shrug. "If you don't think you can write a good paper, then there's not much point in turning one in."

"I didn't say I couldn't write a good paper," Jenny protested irritably. "I just said I wasn't interested in trying."

"Umm, I see. Well, I suppose you'll have to decide whether or not you think it's worth the effort, won't you?"

"Oh, I guess it is," Jenny muttered. "My grades in history are pretty good, so there's no use failing the course by not turning in a term paper."

"Makes sense to me," Anne answered absently. Tucking her book beneath one arm, she slipped her hands into the pockets of her jeans and glanced casually around the room, noticing the messy book-covered desk in the far right corner. She inclined her head in that direction. "Is that what you've been doing up here all weekend—making notes for your report?"

"Some of the time." Turning over, Jenny sat up on the edge of her bed and flicked a strand of long, dark hair back over her shoulder. "Why do you ask? Do you think I might have been sneaking out of the house by climbing out my window and down a ladder?"

Anne laughed softly. "To tell the truth, that thought never occurred to me. But maybe it should have. Is that what you've been doing?"

Apparently not pleased by the way the conversation was going, Jenny tensed, balling her hands into fists at her sides. "You're not fooling me one bit, you know," she said sharply. "I know exactly why you're here. I'm not stupid."

"I never imagined you were," Anne replied frankly. "I was pretty sure you'd realize I'm here to keep an eye on you when your brother can't be here himself."

Jenny's mouth nearly fell open. "You mean you admit it!"

"There wouldn't be much point in trying to lie, would there? I know you're not that gullible."

"Well, at least you're honest," Jenny muttered begrudgingly. Then uttering a frustrated oath, she slapped her palm against one bedpost and curled her fingers so tightly around it that her knuckles became white. "Ooh, why can't Ty just mind his own business and let me live my own life? What I do is no concern of his."

"I think it is," Anne said gently. "You are his sister and he cares about you."

"Oh fiddlesticks!" Jenny exploded, jumping to her feet. "He never seemed very interested in me until Daddy died. In fact, Ty lived in his own apartment in Alexandria until Daddy's accident. He and I don't really know each other very well. So why has he developed this sudden interest in me?"

"As I said, you're his sister and he loves you. If the two of you were never close, I imagine it was because he's quite a few years older than you are."

"Well, that's true," Jenny conceded reluctantly, but a deep frown marred her brow. "But even so, he has no right to try to tell me what to do. I don't care if he is my brother."

"I really don't understand your attitude," Anne said quietly. "Why do you resent Ty?"

"Because he's not my father, but he's trying to act like he is!" Marching across the room, Jenny went to stare out into the darkness beyond the window. "He tries to boss me around and refuses to let me do what I want to do. But he's not Daddy and he'll never take Daddy's place, no matter how hard he tries. I just wish he'd leave me alone. I'm grown up now, and I don't need a father, which is a good thing isn't it, since I don't have one anymore?"

As Jenny's voice broke revealingly, tears of sympathy sprang to Anne's eyes. She moved across the room to stand beside the girl at the window. "You're really missing him, aren't you? I know how you feel."

"Oh, no you don't!" Jenny snapped, jerking her head around to stare at Anne impatiently. "You couldn't possibly know how I feel!"

"Oh, but I do. My father died when I was seventeen, too."

Regret flickered over Jenny's face, then she bent her head and stared at the floor. "I'm sorry. I didn't know," she murmured almost inaudibly. "So I guess you *do* know how I feel."

"Yes. Very lost and confused and a little angry that it had to be your father who died and not somebody else's," Anne suggested softly. "You hate to feel that way, but you do. And you wonder if you always did enough to let your father know you cared about him." As Jenny stifled a sob, Anne touched her shoulder lightly. "Everything you're feeling is perfectly natural, but you can't take your unhappiness out on other people, especially the ones who care about you. I think you should remember that your father was Ty's father, too. His loss was as great as yours."

"But Daddy and I were so close," Jenny said, her voice thick. "You see, he and Mother didn't think they could have another child after Ty, but when he was nearly seventeen, I came along and my father was ecstatic. He'd always wanted a daughter." She smiled rather sheepishly. "I have to admit he did pamper me and give me almost anything I wanted. And we did things together."

"My father and I did, too," Anne said, her voice lowering reminiscently. "I was his first born, and since he really expected me to be a son, he just decided to treat me like one. He took me fishing with him and bragged to his friends that I could bait a hook better than any boy he'd ever seen. We had great times together. He was a farmer and, much to my mother's dismay, he taught me to drive a tractor by the time I was eight."

Jenny laughed and a vibrant animation erased the sulky unhappiness that was usually in her face. "You must have had a lot of fun with him. My father was a lot of fun to be with, too." Her smile faded and she sighed. "We were just so close. I don't think Ty understands how I feel now that he's gone."

"I'm sure he does. Ty was close to your father, too," Anne tried to explain. "They worked together at Manning Consultants, and they always seemed to me to have a very wonderful relationship. So, try to remember that Ty is probably missing him as much as you are."

Jenny shrugged, apparently unwilling to admit that fact as yet. Young as she was, she could only perceive her own grief and she assumed it was far greater than that felt by anyone else. Almost defensively, as if she didn't want to allow herself to think about anyone else, Jenny steered the conversation back to her previous argument. "Well, I don't know how Ty feels. All I know is that he can't take Daddy's place with me. He can't order me around. I'll do what I want and go out with anybody I please."

"If you mean Kirt Callen, then Ty's doing you a real favor by telling you not to see him," Anne said bluntly. "You don't want to get involved with a man like that. He's a notorious playboy, and you're too young for him."

"He likes younger women," Jenny said self-righteously. "He says we're more natural and more fun and lots less cynical than older women."

"I bet he did. That sounds like a well-practiced line to me. Don't you realize men like him will say anything they think women want to hear?" Anne shuddered slightly, finding the mere thought of Kirt Callen disagreeable. "But no matter what he says, he's not the right man for you. He has no respect for women. He only wants to use them. He's . . ."

"I don't want to hear what you think of him," Jenny

interrupted tersely, flouncing away to sprawl across the bed again. "How do I know you're not just trying to make me dislike him because you're interested in him yourself?"

"Take my word for it. I'll never compete with you for his attention. He's not my type, I assure you," Anne said flatly, walking across to stand at the foot of the bed as she gently added, "And he's not your type either. . . ."

"I'm busy," Jenny cut in, making a great show of straightening the papers in front of her on the bed. "Do you mind?"

Sighing inwardly, Anne shook her head, knowing she would get nowhere fast if she tried to make Jenny listen. Patience was what the girl needed, and to win her trust, Anne knew she dare not sermonize. At least tonight they had started to become acquainted, and that was a beginning. After saying goodnight and getting no response at all from Jenny, Anne quietly left the room.

It was only about nine-thirty, too early for bed, so Anne went back downstairs to the comfortable study. Soon she was engrossed again in the mystery novel she was reading, and by the time she extricated herself from the baffling tangle of clues, over an hour had passed. She was getting sleepy and, wanting a long hot bath before bed, she decided to go up to her own bedroom.

As she walked through the wide hall toward the stairs a moment later, she heard the sound of a key turning in the front door lock and halted her steps. She turned just as the door swung open and Ty stepped inside, carrying a tan leather suitcase in one lean hand. To her dismay, the mere sight of him was catalyst enough to make her heart start a crazy palpitating beat. It was a purely involuntary physical reaction, one she was powerless to control, but she berated herself for responding to him like a foolish adolescent.

Suddenly he looked up and saw her standing there. After allowing his narrowed gaze to wander lazily over the length of her body, he gave her one of those slow, easy smiles, which only served to make her heart beat even more erratically. Nonetheless, she smiled back at him as he strode down the hall to join her at the foot of the stairs. When he stopped close in front of her, she detected the now-familiar lime fragrance of his after-shave. Stilling the ridiculously urgent desire to touch him, she tilted her head to one side inquiringly. "How was your trip?"

"Not bad," he answered, holding her gaze. "The owner of the land the Petersons wanted to purchase out there finally came to terms. And how about you? How was your weekend? Did Jenny give you any trouble?"

"None at all. In fact, she never left the house. I was surprised," Anne admitted. "But I think we should be relieved. Since she didn't seem at all interested in going out, she can't be very involved with Kirt Callen. But I do suspect she talked to him on the phone several times, though I can't be absolutely positive. She took all the calls in her room, where she spent most of the weekend."

Ty unbuttoned his tan suit jacket and his vest, then removed his tobacco brown tie, while never once looking away from Anne. "I suppose she knows why you're here?" he questioned matter-of-factly. "Is that why she stayed up in her room? Didn't you get any chance at all to talk to her?"

"We talked tonight, for the first time." Anne went on to relate in detail her conversation with his sister, then finished by saying, "And yes, she knows exactly why

I'm here. She confronted me with it, and I didn't lie to her. I told her I was indeed here to keep an eye on her."

"That's probably best," Ty said simply, cupping Anne's elbow in one hand as he guided her up the stairs. "Though my sister is acting immaturely these days, she's nobody's fool. It wouldn't have been a good idea to lie to her about your reason for being here. But how did she react when you admitted you were keeping an eye on her? Did she seem to resent it?"

Anne smiled. "I did get the impression that she wanted to call me a spy, but she expressed more of a resentment toward life in general than she did toward me in particular. It's so obvious to me that she needs someone to talk to. I think, with luck, she might be willing to be a bit more friendly with me. Not right away, but eventually."

Pausing at the head of the stairs, Ty turned Anne toward him. "You see, I knew I was making a wise move by bringing you here," he said softly. "You know how to deal with a girl Jenny's age, while I lack a great deal of expertise in that area, I'm afraid."

"Don't count your chickens before they're hatched," she advised him wryly. "I haven't won Jenny's trust yet."

"But you will," he informed her, escorting her along the corridor to the left. "I have faith in you. You've already had one good idea—about taking her to St. Croix with me. I'm going to invite her this week. Let's just hope she says yes."

As they stopped at her room, he stepped across the hall, opened the door directly across from hers, and put his suitcase down on the floor just inside the dark room. Anne's eyes widened slightly and her heart, which had finally begun to behave normally again, now recommenced those thudding palpitations. It had never occurred to her that his room might be so close to her own, and though she knew she shouldn't let his proximity bother her, it very definitely did. Unable to look directly at him when he moved back across the hall toward her, she feigned a great interest in a blue-glazed delft vase on the small mahogany table beside her door, then gestured hesitantly. "Well, you must be tired after that long flight, so I'll just say goodnight."

"Not so fast, Anne. I'm not that tired." Catching her by one hand, he drew her toward him. His fingers came up to brush over the sensitive skin beneath her widening eyes. "And you look much less tired now," he said, his voice deep and melodious. "No more dark circles."

"I . . . do feel more like a human being," she admitted, bracing herself not to react to his disturbing touch. "Maybe I *was* trying to work too many hours a day."

Ty didn't answer. His fingertips traced the contours of her cheeks, then sought the wisp of golden hair that brushed her temple. Rubbing the silken strand between his fingers, he whispered softly, "Your hair's like spun gold."

Anne held her breath as every inch of her skin burned with her knowledge that his eyes were sweeping over her. She felt as if she were standing naked before him. At last she could bear the intense appraisal no longer. She looked up at his tan face, until finally his blue eyes met hers. "Why must you always look at me that way when I wear jeans?" she asked defensively. "Surely you don't think they're inappropriate attire for me here? If I'm going to live in this house, I think I should be allowed to dress comfortably. Up at your mountain house, it was different. We were there on business, so I understood why you expected me to wear my office clothes. But here . . ."

A wave of his hand silenced her immediately, as he stared at her with the utmost confusion. Then, after a few seconds, understanding gentled his finely carved features, and shaking his head, he smiled. "If you didn't wear jeans that weekend in the mountains because you thought I didn't approve, then you were sadly mistaken, Anne."

"But I . . ."

"Frankly, I was disappointed when you changed that afternoon to your pristine little skirt and blouse. And I was even more disappointed when you never wore the jeans again the entire time we were up there." He smiled mischievously. "If I stared at you that day, I'm sorry. It was only because I'd never seen you dressed so casually before, but I certainly didn't mean to convey disapproval. On the contrary, I distinctly remember thinking that you have the perfect . . . uh, shape to look fantastic in jeans."

Tapping her forefinger against her lips, Anne looked at him with some suspicion. Usually he was an unfathomable man, his expression frustratingly unreadable, but this time, she realized, there was no mistaking the appreciative glimmer dancing in his blue eyes. And, having detected the suggestive note in his half-serious remark about her shape, she shook her head at him. "Really, Mr. Manning, I'm surprised at you," she said, exaggerating a prudish tone. "A busy man like you shouldn't waste time thinking about what is or isn't the perfect . . . uh, shape for jeans."

Ty stepped closer. "You think not?"

"Absolutely," she retorted primly, turning swiftly to step inside her room. And as Ty playfully swatted her derriere, she spun around, trying to stare at him indignantly. That was impossible, however, and she found herself returning his teasing grin before she pushed the door firmly shut.

Thirty minutes later after a relaxing, scented bath, Anne left the bathroom that adjoined her bedroom and went immediately to turn back the quilted rust-colored coverlet on the antique carved-mahogany bed. As she yawned behind her hand, she stepped out of her slippers. A moment later, when she heard a loud thumping noise in the hall, she padded barefoot across her room, opened the door and looked out, just in time to see Jenny gather up the books she had dropped and then disappear down the stairs. As Anne started to close her door again, Ty's was suddenly opened. When his dark brows lifted questioningly, she explained. "It was Jenny. She dropped some books on her way downstairs."

"Downstairs?" he repeated somewhat suspiciously.

Anne smiled. "I don't think she was planning to go out anywhere in those very skimpy short pajamas she was wearing. No doubt she's gone to the kitchen. Teenagers must have late night snacks from time to time."

Ty's answering smile faded almost immediately as he gazed at Anne. Though she was unaware of it, the light from the bedside lamp behind her silhouetted the enticing curves of her slender body beneath her thin white batiste nightgown.

As his narrowed gaze roamed slowly over her, she sensed a sudden, still tension in him that alerted her to danger. Her breath caught. Before she could step back and close the door, he strode across the hall into her room, diminishing the distance between them so swiftly that her heart lurched painfully against her breastbone. He, himself, pushed the door shut.

"*Ty,*" she began, but her words were halted by the finger he pressed against her lips. Then his hand dropped down. His fingertips traced the low, square neckline of her gown, scorching her creamy skin, his touch lingering on the delightfully firm, yet yielding curve of her breasts. She trembled, knowing she was insane to let him touch her that way, yet helpless to prevent it. She liked the way his caresses made her feel: warm and week and acquiescent. Yet, uncertainty widened her gray eyes, when his hands spanned her waist and he abruptly drew her against the hard length of his body.

"*Anne,*" he whispered unevenly, and the hint of appeal in his tone was irresistible. As his arms tightened around her, she melted against him, her own arms slipping beneath his unbuttoned shirt, her hands spreading open on his strong smooth back, urging him nearer. It was as if she couldn't get close enough, a feeling he obviously shared. Arching her to him, he boldly explored her body, molding with lean seeking hands the softly curving contours and following the delightful insweep of her small waist. Then his mouth was on hers, firm and possessive, parting the tender softness of her lips with ravishing intensity.

Anne moaned softly as he tasted the sweetness within her mouth, and one strong hand clasped the back of her head, holding her fast as his kiss deepened. Her lips clung to his. Her mouth opened wider to the invading exploration of the tip of his tongue. Winding her braid around his hand, he tilted her head back again and trailed burning kisses down her slender neck to the racing pulse, and lower, to the scented hollow at the base of her throat. His teeth, gently nipping her creamy skin, aroused every nerve ending in her, making his touch no longer just delightful, but also necessary. Her trembling fingers traced the muscular contours of his broad back, and as she moved against him, a muffled groan came from deep in his throat.

"Let me take your hair down, Anne," he whispered. And before she could react, he moved closer still, slipping his fingers into the loose braid and threading them through the strands until her hair cascaded in golden disarray over her shoulders like a skein of pure silk. His fingers tangled in it, tilting her head back farther. "Lovely. You're so lovely," he muttered roughly, his lips burning across her cheek. "Anne, I need you."

She needed him, too, and as his hard mouth covered hers with persuasive power, she could no longer deny that need. When the softness of her body came together with the long length of his, her newly discovered love for him blazed out of control for a few ecstatic minutes. His kiss seemed an endless act of possession itself, his lips capturing the soft sweetness of hers, not only taking pleasure, but also giving. An aching desire to give herself completely and irrevocably to him spread a weakening warmth through her lower limbs. Her small hands moved feverishly across his broad shoulders to explore the tendons of his neck, her fingers probing his heated flesh, evoking a soft groan from him.

Large, lean hands roved freely over her, cupping and caressing her soft breasts until they surged tautly against his palms. Then his hands moved down to mold her rounded hips, pressing her to his muscular thighs. Her lips moved eagerly beneath his. Her trembling fingers tangled in the thick hair on his nape to press his head down, urging a rougher taking of her mouth. Aroused more than she had ever been, she was pliant and receptive to the hand that pressed her flat abdomen, then brushed, too fleetingly, over her breasts.

Ty lowered one strap of her gown. His questing lips sought the delicate hollows of her shoulders, tantalizing her sensitized skin. "Anne, I want you," he groaned, before taking her mouth once again.

His kiss deepened with near-savage urgency as his words echoed in her head, and suddenly he swept her up in his arms and carried her to the bed. He put her down gently on the cool sheet, then came down beside her, covering her slight body with the stronger length of his. His hands cupped her small face as his lips plundered the moist tenderness of hers. Oddly, unsteady fingers lowered her gown, baring her rapidly rising and falling breasts as he lifted his dark head to gaze down at her.

"God, you're exquisite," he muttered huskily, his breathing ragged, searing desire burning fiercely blue in his eyes.

With his first touch, Anne tensed instinctively, but when his brushing fingers took possession of her full, rounded breasts, she succumbed to the hot fire that sparkled over her skin. He traced the satin-textured roseate peaks until they hardened beneath his fingertips. His dark head lowered. His mouth closed around one throbbing crest, pulling gently. Anne gasped as the aching emptiness within her intensified unbearably, clamoring for a satisfaction only he could give. When he nibbled the sensitized, ever-hardening peak and pressed down one muscular thigh demandingly, parting hers, the very intensity of the thrill that pulsated through her restored her sanity. Much as she wanted him, she was emotionally unready for complete surrender. Her breath coming in soft, fast gasps, she pushed at his shoulders. "Ty, no," she whispered. "I . . . I can't. I just can't."

With a soft groan, he turned over, sat up on the edge of the bed for several long seconds, then stood to gaze down at her, an odd mixture of tenderness, impatience and desire burning in his eyes. As she hastily covered her bared breasts with her arms, she couldn't be sure if his slight smile was mocking or indulgent. Then, without a word, he strode across the room and out the door.

Pressing her fingers against lips still parted and

tingling from his kisses, she moaned softly. "Fool," she bleakly called herself aloud. Now she had done what she had sworn to herself she would never do again. She had gone far beyond breaking the rule against kissing the boss—she had committed the ultimate folly of falling in love with him.

Chapter Seven

The next Saturday, Sue unexpectedly visited the Manning house. To Anne's delight and surprise, her sister and Jenny took an instant liking to each other. Despite Jenny's usual protestations about people her age being too immature and silly, she didn't seem to see Sue that way. Taking advantage of that fact, Anne impulsively suggested they all go into Alexandria on a shopping trip. And an astonishing miracle occurred—Jenny agreed to go.

"I'll just dash upstairs and change clothes," she said, grimacing at the cut-off jeans and halter top she was wearing. "I can hardly go to town in these, but I'll be back down in a jiffy. Don't leave without me."

"We'd never do that. In fact, Sue will go upstairs with you while you change," Anne told her and was rewarded with a genuinely grateful smile. Watching Sue follow as Jenny immediately bounded out of the study; acting for the first time as a seventeen-year-old girl should, Anne breathed a sign of relief. Perhaps she was beginning to win the girl's trust at last.

Using the time while the two girls were gone, Anne began to tidy the papers on Ty's desk, then tensed involuntarily when he unexpectedly entered the study. She watched him warily as he approached her, but his expression gave her no indication of what sort of mood he was in. Sometimes he treated her with such warmth that she couldn't resist him. Then, at other times, he acted as if he was lord of all and she was his slave, obliged to obey his every command. He kept her continually on edge, because she never knew from one moment to the next what his attitude toward her would be. And as he camc toward her now, her wide gray eyes mirrored her uncertainty.

Ty, however, eased her tension somewhat when he smiled casually, then sat down on the edge of the desk. While he idly examined a brass letter opener, Anne feigned a great interest in the papers she was arranging, though in reality she was wondering where he had been all morning. With Millicent Beaumont?

"Is Jenny hiding in her room again?" Ty inquired finally, breaking the silence. "When I came home, I noticed her MG was still here."

"She's in her room, but not hiding this time," Anne told him, enthusiasm illuminating her delicate features, as she went on to explain that his sister had agreed to go shopping with Sue and her. "That's a step in the right direction, don't you think?"

He nodded, his warm gaze wandering slowly over her. "I knew you'd be good for Jenny," he said, his voice low and appealingly rough. "I think you may even be able to convince her to forget about Kirt Callen."

"Well, I haven't succeeded in that, yet. She still talks on the phone to him frequently," Anne admitted, regret darkening her eyes. "He's trying his best to take advantage of her confusion about your father's death, but I'm hoping she's beginning to have reservations about him. No doubt he would like to seduce her, but she hasn't succumbed to the seduction, yet. Frankly, I don't think she really wants to."

"I hope you're right," Ty replied somberly, then shrugged. "At least it's a good sign that she didn't object to going to St. Croix with me next weekend. Though she's always loved to go there, I half expected her to rebel when I told her I wanted her to join me this time. I was pleasantly surprised when she agreed to the idea so readily."

"That is a relief."

"Since this is a business trip, I'll expect you to accompany me, too, Anne," he said firmly, his narrowed eyes searching her face. "In the capacity of secretary, of course."

Anne's cheeks darkened to an enticing pink. She was completely unprepared for the idea of spending the weekend with Ty in such a romantic setting. But before she could formulate a sufficiently businesslike answer, the phone on the desk rang, providing her with a brief reprieve. She swiftly picked up the receiver. "Oh hello, Mike," she responded after a moment. "Dinner? This evening?" Before she could diplomatically refuse his invitation, hard fingers clamped her right wrist in a vise-like grip. Startled, she turned to look at Ty, who was glaring grimly at her.

"Tell Mike thanks, but no thanks," he commanded curtly, his voice low. "You're not going out to dinner with him. Tell him that."

Resentment stormed in Anne's gray eyes. Her uptilted chin challenged his right to issue orders, yet his piercing gaze warned her not to be foolish enough to voice that challenge. Sheer rebellion tempted her to consider accepting Mike's invitation, though that hadn't been her intention. Caution at last overcame her desire to rebel. In a strained voice, she told Mike she had already made plans for the evening, an excuse he accepted easily, as friends do.

When the telephone call ended a moment later, Anne replaced the receiver, then yanked her wrist free of Ty's merciless grip. "You don't control my personal life, you know," she uttered resentfully, glowering at him and thinking of his relationship with Millicent. "You go out with whomever you please, and so will I. The next time Mike calls, if I *want* to go out with him, *I will.* You don't own me!"

"But I do pay you to be with Jenny," he countered, his words clipped and cold. "You can't very well keep an eye on her if you're out socializing. Mike Bennett will be going along with us to St. Croix next weekend. I hope that won't prove to be too much of a temptation for you! And another thing, Jenny won't be able to protect you completely. It's a big island, Anne, so you and I will undoubtedly be alone together sometimes. Count on it."

"Promises, promises," she taunted, then caught her breath as he stood to tower over her.

"Yes, it is a promise, Anne," he said too softly. "Remember that."

As if she could forget, she thought, her pulses racing with dizzying rapidity. And it wasn't until he strode out of the study that she finally managed to breathe again.

The next Wednesday evening Anne placed a fat file folder on Ty's desk in the study, then watched as he quickly scanned the documents inside it. A slight frown creased his brow, and he went through the papers a second time, then looked up questioningly at her.

"I didn't see the statement on Bob's cumulative

preferred stocks in here," he told her. "And I'll need to discuss that with him while we're on St. Croix."

Nodding, Anne made a notation on a small memo pad. "I'll have plenty of time to get it from the office tomorrow night before our flight."

"Fine. Other than that, you seem to have everything I wanted," he said, closing the file, then leaning back in his swivel chair and crossing his arms behind his head. "Actually, I don't have a great deal of business to discuss with the Petersons while we're there. That new property we acquired in San Francisco will be the main item of business. I'm looking at the trip more as a holiday for you and me and Jenny."

Anne nodded, relieved his tone was friendly. Apparently their last argument had simply been another low in their roller-coaster relationship, and now he was willing to forget it. So she decided to try to forget it, too. Tugging at the wisp of hair that grazed her cheek, she smiled rather shyly at him. "I just hope Jenny will have a nice time. She needs to have some fun."

"I'm counting on Bob's son, Rob, to show her a nice time. They've known each other since they were kids, and she's fond of him. Besides, she says St. Croix is the most beautiful island in the world. I'm not so sure of that, but it is magnificent. Have you ever been?"

"Oh no, I've always gone home to visit Mom and the girls during my vacations," Anne told him as a certain eager glow of excitement animated her features. "To tell the truth, I've never been anywhere really exotic, so I can hardly wait to see St. Croix."

Straightening in his chair, Ty reached across the desk and caught one small hand in his and drew her around to him. His thumb brushed provocatively over the throbbing pulse in her delicate wrist. "That's one of the things I like about you, Anne," he said softly. "You react to everything with such enthusiasm, even something as simple as going sledding in an unexpected snowfall."

"That's nice of you to say," she answered almost in a whisper, wondering if he knew that she longed for him to take her in his arms. "But my enthusiastic reactions might seem naive and childish to some people."

"Your reactions are enchanting and very refreshing," he declared firmly, then grinned. "And some people are dolts, so we don't worry about what they think. Do we?"

"I never really have," she confessed without apology. And when his hands moved to span her waist, she covered them with her own, brushing her fingers over his as a strange and powerful sense of belonging flooded her being. She felt amazingly happy and content, but just as his hands tightened around her, as if he intended to draw her down onto his lap, the study door opened. Anne stepped back away from him as Jenny ambled into the room.

"I'm all packed," she announced, sliding her hands into the hip pockets of her jeans. Though she wasn't bubbling over with friendliness and good will, there was little sign of the usual resentment in her face as she looked at her brother. "I thought I'd better come down and find out when our flight is, so I'd know what time I have to get up in the morning."

He shrugged. "I don't know the exact departure time. Anne made the reservations," he said, turning to her inquiringly.

"The flight doesn't leave until three in the afternoon," she responded. "So, you'll be able to sleep late in the morning if you want to, Jenny."

"Oh, I do. That's one of the nice things about not having to go to my classes."

"I guess everybody enjoys not having to go to school once in awhile," Anne said, smiling reminiscently.

"But will you miss a lot by skipping two days of classes?"

"What does it matter if I do?" Jenny replied with a careless toss of her hand. "None of the courses I take are all that interesting anyhow. College can be a real drag."

"Maybe it wouldn't be such a drag to you, if you didn't take the right to go to college for granted," Ty remarked curtly, glancing at Anne. Leaning forward in his chair, he rested his arms on the desk and stared at his sister. "You'd be wise to remember that other people have to scrimp and save and sacrifice so they can go to college. I imagine they find their classes less of a drag than you do. You seem to find it very easy to forget how fortunate you are, Jenny."

"Oh, buzz off, Ty," his sister retorted, tossing her head defiantly. "You're always hassling me, and I'm getting plenty tired of it."

"Jenny, be careful what you say," he warned ominously, standing behind his desk. "I don't know exactly what you're trying to prove by your rebellious behavior, but I do know I'd like to turn you over my knee."

"You'd better not even try!" Jenny growled furiously. "If you do, I'll call Mother and tell her what you did."

Just as Anne was searching her brain for some way to halt this argument before it deteriorated into a bitter fight, a knock on the study door provided a perfectly timed diversion. Mrs. Wilkes, the housekeeper, stepped into the room on silent feet. "A young woman to see you, Mr. Manning," she said, and even as she made the announcement, Millicent Beaumont rushed into the study. Spying Ty, she nearly ran to him, clutching his right arm in both her hands and holding on, as if she never meant to let go.

"Ty, I have to talk to you. It's important," she said

urgently, glancing at Jenny and Anne. "But alone, please."

Her insistent tone brought a questioning frown to his brow, but he nodded. "We'll go across the hall."

As Ty and Millicent left the study, Jenny flopped down on the sofa. "My, she sure was eager to see him, wasn't she?"

Nodding, Anne busied herself with the Peterson portfolio, putting it and a few other separate papers into Ty's briefcase. Though she tried not to think anything of Millicent's unexpected visit, the beginnings of uneasiness stirred inside her.

That uneasiness increased considerably a few minutes later, when Ty returncd. "I have to go out for awhile," he said, his expression beyond analysis as he looked at Anne. "And on second thought, we'll also need to get the quitclaim deed for the Mayfair property before we leave tomorrow."

"I'll make a note of it," she answered stiffly, turning back toward the desk. When she heard his footsteps recede in the hall, she felt a hard knot of distress tighten in her stomach.

"Well, well, what do you think of that?" Jenny remarked, her face a study in curiosity. "I wonder what's going on with those two. Could they be starting up again where they left off?"

"I wouldn't know," Anne replied, striving to sound only mildly interested. "Where did they leave off?"

"Oh, Ty and Millicent were very close once," Jenny said matter-of-factly, getting up from the sofa and stretching sleepily. "But then they just drifted apart, and she married somebody else. But I heard she and her husband separated recently. So, who knows, maybe she and Ty will get back together."

"Yes, who knows," Anne repeated dully. Biting down hard on her lower lip, she pretended to be searching for something in the briefcase on the desk. And she only managed to muster a semblance of a smile as Jenny yawned loudly.

"It's deadly dull around here," the younger girl complained, then shrugged. "I think I'll just go up to bed."

"All right. Sleep well," Anne murmured, as Jenny walked out of the study, totally unaware of the pain her innocent comments had inflicted.

Chapter Eight

On Friday morning Anne awoke to the sweet sound of birds singing in the lemon and mango trees outside her window. Soft early-morning sunlight streamed between the slats of the shutters, creating a linear design of light and shadow on her bed. The long, thick fringe of her lashes fluttered as she struggled to open her eyes, but when she abruptly remembered she was actually on the exotic island of St. Croix, excitement brought her fully awake. She sat up and stretched her shapely bare arms above her head. Glancing at the bed next to hers, she found that Jenny had buried her head beneath her pillow to escape the light.

Slipping out of bed, Anne tiptoed to the pale blue tiled bathroom that she and Jenny shared in the Peterson's guest bungalow. Ty had a room and bath to himself across the hall, while Mike Bennett was booked into a hotel. After washing her face, Anne brushed her teeth, then tugged off the elastic band that secured the thick braid of her hair. Standing before the large gold-framed mirror that met the built-in marble vanity, she proceeded to brush the silken strands briskly until they lay softly about her shoulders, shimmering like gold with a healthy sheen. With deft fingers she replaited her hair and pinned it into a chignon on her nape.

Back in the bedroom, she quickly dressed in a navy sailcloth back-wrap skirt and white cotton-knit sweater, which she thought would be suitable attire for the meeting she, Ty and Mike were to have with Bob Peterson later in the morning. After stepping into cork-heeled leather sandals, she picked up her sunglasses from the dressing table and tiptoed out of the room. Ty's door was still closed and, detecting no sound inside his room, she glided quietly down the hall past the diminutive kitchen and through the bungalow's great room.

Even before she could push open the screened front door and step onto the shaded veranda, she caught the combined fragrances of the sweet white jasmine and the scarlet bougainvillea vines that climbed the veranda columns. She ran lightly down the stairs to the flagstone walk that cut through the lush green lawn scattered with lemon trees. The clean citrus scent of their white blossoms mingled with the perfume of the flowers and the saltiness of the ocean air, and Anne took a deep, refreshing breath.

It had been nearly dusk when they arrived on St. Croix the night before, so this morning was her first opportunity to see the island in daylight. It was beautiful. Bordering the Peterson estate on three sides was a lush subtropical forest where occasional tall mahogany trees towered above the smaller logwood and bay trees. Both the main house and the bungalow faced the sea, and as Anne followed the winding path that led to the reef, she was dazzled by the shimmer of sunlight on the wide expanse of water before her. This was the ocean as she had never before seen it—crystal clear and sapphire blue. Waves broke in a creamy froth on the beach and beckoned to her.

A natural stairway of sorts had formed in the reef, and after picking her way cautiously to the bottom, she removed her sandals and stepped barefoot into the cool sand. In May the rays of the sun were not yet intensely hot, and their warmth now was tempered by a caressing trade wind that stirred the tendril of hair at her cheek. Tall coconut palms swayed in the breeze, their long, stiff fronds whispering against one another.

At the water's edge Anne warily dipped one toe in the foamy surf and found it delightfully warm. Wading toward the reef that edged the far end of the beach, she smiled as the soft waves broke over her feet, then sucked the sand from beneath her toes with their ebbing flow. Slipping her hands into the pockets of her skirt, she breathed a sigh. Something in the natural beauty of this secluded reef-enclosed cove drew her thoughts to Ty and to her feelings for him.

Since Wednesday night, when he had left his house with Millicent, Anne had tried desperately not to think about him. To some extent, she had succeeded. Thursday morning in Alexandria had been spent in preparations for the trip and to her surprise, she had slept away a good deal of the flight to St. Croix. Then, on their arrival, the excitement of meeting the Petersons had diverted her thoughts, as had getting settled in the bungalow later Thursday evening. When bedtime had come, she had fallen asleep almost the moment her head touched the pillow. But now she was wondering if perhaps sleep was becoming a defense mechanism that allowed her to escape from her distressing thoughts.

Once she had realized she had fallen in love with Ty, her feelings for him had intensified with breathtaking swiftness. Now, as she walked along the beach, she felt hopelessly trapped by the love she felt for him. Until the past few weeks, she had always led a structured life, but now she knew she no longer had sole control of her destiny. Self-discipline had been relatively easy when her main goal in life had been to see Sue through college. Now, though she still cared deeply about her sister's education, she realized her life was not so one-dimensional. She had needs of her own, and falling in love had awakened those needs. They nagged at her relentlessly, sweeping her up in a turmoil of emotions that she was powerless to control. Simply being near Ty was both a pleasure and an agony. There was a happiness in loving him, but it was bittersweet. She needed his tenderness and his passion and, most importantly, his love, but that didn't mean he would ever be able to return her feeling. Life was just not so simple.

Stopping for a moment in the water that frothed about her slender ankles, she lifted her face to the sun and allowed her troubled gaze to drift with the milk white clouds that sailed across a brilliant blue sky. Then she walked on again, breathing another sigh. Why had she fallen in love with him? She hadn't wanted to, knowing he was a man totally beyond her reach. Yet, little by little, day by day, liking and respect had deepened to become an irrevocable love. Knowing herself as the serious person she was, Anne was afraid that she would never stop loving him, although he couldn't love her. She didn't want to live with unrequited passion all the rest of her life.

If only she had exercised more self-discipline in her relationship with him, she chided herself mentally. Then suddenly, she took a sharp, startled breath as two large hands descended onto her shoulders. Jerking her head around, she found Ty behind her, smiling one of those lazy, slow smiles as her wide eyes met the clear blue of his. All thoughts of self-discipline were swamped by her overwhelming love for him and an answering smile trembled on her softly shaped lips.

In silence his nearly mesmerizing gaze darkened and held hers for several spellbinding seconds, but at last he spoke, his deep voice melodious. "I didn't expect to find you up and out so early, but maybe I should have. After all, you once found an early morning snow equally irresistible." As he glanced down at his rolled up khaki trouser legs and his bare feet, his smile deepened. "You know, you have this amazing ability to make me revert to childhood. First, you tempt me into riding downhill on a sled, and now I find myself wading in the ocean."

With a knowing grin, Anne retorted lightly, "I suspect I didn't have to do much tempting. If you didn't want to go sledding or wading in the first place, I'm sure I couldn't persuade you."

"I suspect you're right," he admitted, draping one arm across her shoulders to turn her toward the sea. "Well, what do you think of it? Does it make you want to go in for a swim?"

"It's magnificent," she murmured. "You were right—I've never seen water so blue. And yes, it does make me want to go for a swim, but I suppose you're going to be a slave driver and make me work before I get to have any fun."

Smiling down at her, he drew her closer and tugged gently at the wisp of hair grazing her temple. "Oh, I intend for you to have fun while we're here, but you're right—I'm a firm believer in business before pleasure, in most instances anyway. Once we've finished going over Bob's financial affairs with him, we'll be free to enjoy ourselves to the fullest. Who knows, maybe you'll relax enough to shed all those inhibitions of yours."

"I wasn't aware that you think I'm inhibited."

"Cautious then, or maybe a little shy."

All of a sudden, his tone had become too serious, and Anne shook her head. "Me, shy? Never," she insisted and to prove her point, she playfully tickled his lean sides. Since he was caught off guard by her action, he released her and she quickly escaped him, running out of the surf and across the sand toward the line of palm trees.

She didn't get far before he caught her, and they both were laughing as he pulled her around into his arms. With that first electric touch of her softly curved body against the harder, stronger length of his, his laughter became an urgent whispering of her name. Gripping her waist in lean demanding hands, he pressed her back against the trunk of a palm tree. As her lips parted, his descended to take their sweetness with dizzyingly persuasive power.

Loving desire to be close to him overshadowed all Anne's doubts, and she responded with an ardor that might have appalled her in its intensity had she been thinking clearly. Instead, she could only delight in the gentle insistence conveyed by the hard hands that roamed over her and found the enticing feminine arch between her slender waist and the outward curving of her hips. Her fingers tangled in his thick dark hair, and she pressed closer to him. In that tantalizing moment in time, she would have eagerly given herself completely to him and, at last, it was he who reluctantly drew away.

His breathing was uneven as he leaned his forehead against hers. "Fantastic as this is, it isn't the right time or place," he whispered huskily, his hard mouth gentling with a smile. "Besides, we're not getting any work done this way, and I don't want to have to think about business tonight or tomorrow or tomorrow night. I'll only want to think about us. So why don't we go get some breakfast right now. Are you hungry?"

"Famished," Anne lied, unwilling to let him know that food was the last thing on her mind.

Most of Anne's afternoon was free. About two o'clock, while Ty finished discussing a few final details with Bob Peterson, she went back to the bungalow to get into her black maillot. After slipping on a terry-cloth beach jacket over it, she stuffed a towel into a straw beach bag, put on her sunglasses, and walked down to the secluded cove she had visited that morning.

Jenny, Mike, and Rob Peterson were already there, and judging by the amount of laughter that accompanied their splashing in the surf, they were having a good time. As Anne spread her towel on the sand, she smiled to herself. Jenny seemed happy here on St. Croix. Rob, nineteen, teased Jenny unmercifully, and she apparently loved every minute of it.

Unable to wait any longer to test the crystal blue water, Anne removed her sunglasses, dropped them carelessly onto the towel, and ran lightly into the foaming surf. Plunging in up to her shoulders, she pushed off and swam to more placid water beyond the breaking waves. Brisk, even strokes took her smoothly through the water, and when her arms and legs began to tire, she turned over onto her back and floated upon the gently rolling surface.

She wasn't allowed to enjoy such peace for long, however. Within a few minutes she was commandeered by Rob Peterson to participate in a crazy game of water polo that apparently had no rules and, therefore, no semblance of order.

"Tackling is not allowed in this game," she laughingly chided Rob when he wrapped one arm around her waist and unceremoniously tossed her aside to prevent her from catching the ball Jenny threw her way. When she surfaced, spluttering, water streaming off her face, she glared at the young man with mock indignation. "That was a foul."

"It most certainly was not," he retorted, swiping his shock of sun-bleached blond hair back from his tanned forehead. "This is called 'free-for-all' water polo. I just invented it, and the only rule is anything goes."

And practically anything did. Finally, teammates Jenny and Anne began to complain loudly that they were being physically abused by the superior strength of the men's team. New arrangements were made, putting Anne and Rob against Jenny and Mike, but the men clowned around so much that there was never any sense of order in the game. At last, Anne was tackled by Mike and she called a halt. "I've had enough. Go tackle Jenny. She seems to enjoy it when you do."

"And I enjoy tackling her. She's a good-looking kid," he retorted with unabashed enthusiasm.

Pleased Mike was attracted to Jenny, Anne smiled as she trudged toward shore, wrapping her braid of hair around her hand to squeeze the excess water from it. Mike was the kind of man who would bolster Jenny's confidence without taking advantage of her. Looking up from the frothing surf, she caught her breath. Ty was standing by her towel, watching her approach with great interest.

Suddenly, she felt stark naked. The swimsuit she wore might have been considered quite modest by some standards, but she still felt very vulnerable in it. She could almost feel Ty's gaze burn her skin as it traveled over her. Her self-consciousness merely intensified as she forced herself to look at him. The white swim trunks he wore accentuated the bronze darkness of his skin, and there was no mistaking the lithe strength in his lean, yet muscular, body.

She sank down quickly onto the towel and smiled wanly when he kneeled beside her. But he didn't return the smile, and when she detected something akin to impatience glinting in his blue eyes, she swallowed with difficulty.

"Having fun?" he asked abruptly, his voice too low, his tone almost accusing.

Her eyes widened slightly as she nodded. "The water's terrific. And, as you can see, Jenny's having a fabulous time. I'm glad you were able to arrange this trip. It'll do her good to have two young men vying for her attention."

"Mike doesn't seem all that interested in Jenny, frankly," Ty replied. "From what I could see, you were the sole focus of his attention."

"Only because I had the ball," she answered flatly. "He wanted it."

"He seemed to be wanting a great deal more to me," Ty grated out.

Her luminous gray eyes searched his lean face as she wondered if he was actually feeling a bit jealous. It would have been exhilarating to believe that he was, but she was not that self-confident. Perhaps he was only perturbed because he wanted Jenny to benefit from all Mike's attention. With a little shrug, she patted her face dry with a small towel she had brought along. "You know how Mike is," she said softly. "Very playful. Look at him now, chasing Jenny."

Ty didn't answer but did appear to relax somewhat. Sitting down on the towel, he leaned back on his elbows, turning his gaze from the sea to Anne as she stretched out beside him.

Anne had closed her eyes, but they shot open again

almost immediately as, without warning, Ty's fingers slipped around to the back of her neck to undo the cords that kept her swimsuit securely in place. Her breath caught deep in her throat when his hard knuckles grazed the rounded curves of her breasts, as he then tied the cords into a small bow at the top of the suit. There was something so provocatively intimate in the gesture that she felt the insane need to cover his hands with hers and press them down against her, but, of course, that was a need she managed to suppress. She felt impaled by his piercing blue eyes and was unable to prevent an entrancing pink color from tinting her cheeks.

Ty smiled slightly. "You have very lovely shoulders, Miss Fairchild," he teased, then lay down beside her without another word.

Some time later Anne drifted off to sleep beneath the hot sun and was awakened by a tickling sensation along her high cheekbones and the bridge of her small nose. Her eyelids slowly opened.

Propped up on one elbow, Ty was gently running one finger over her skin. "You're getting a nice sprinkling of freckles."

Wrinkling her nose, she sat up and rummaged through her beach bag for a bottle of sunscreen lotion. Finding that her skin was becoming faintly pink, she smoothed the lotion over her arms and legs, and especially over her nose and cheeks, to avoid adding more freckles to her latest collection. Then, as she began to rub the sunscreen across her bared shoulders, Ty took the bottle from her hand.

"Turn over," he commanded softly. "I'll do your back."

As she obeyed and lay on her stomach, resting her chin on her folded arms, the elasticized top of her swimsuit began to creep slowly down. It went lower and lower, and she held her breath, hoping it would stop so she wouldn't have to awkwardly pull it back up again. At last the slow nerve-wracking slide ceased and left her safely covered. She was able to breathe again, though not very deeply as Ty's hands began to stroke her back. His touch was not impersonal. Even after the lotion had been smoothed into her satin-textured skin, his hands lingered, his strong, lean fingers trailing along her spine and exploring the delicately structured contours of her back. A delightful weakness invaded her limbs, but as his fingertips brushed over the firmly rounded sides of her breasts, exposed by the traitorous swimsuit, she trembled slightly and Ty immediately removed his hands.

"I think we'd better go for a swim," he suggested gruffly. And when Anne turned over, hastily hitched up the top of her suit, then tied the cords at the back of her neck again, his burning gaze never left her for an instant.

The presence of Jenny, Mike and Rob helped make the remainder of the afternoon tension-free, at least for Anne. But they abandoned her immediately after dinner that evening. When Rob took Mike and Jenny out to meet some of his friends, Anne and Ty were left alone with the elder Petersons, who were both very likable, unpretentious people. Anne enjoyed talking to them, and the time passed so quickly that she was quite surprised when Ty glanced at his wristwatch and informed her it was past eleven.

"And remember, I promised you that moonlight swim," he added nonchalantly, then smiled at their hosts. "Anne's never been swimming at night in the Caribbean, so I thought her first time should be tonight."

First time for what! Anne thought frantically. She had never agreed to any moonlight swim! As she stood up beside him, she smiled rather nervously at the Petersons. "I . . . enjoyed dinner. Thank you for asking me to join you."

After adding his thanks, Ty lost no time guiding Anne out of the main house, but he said nothing as they walked through the moonlight to the bungalow. Once inside, he led her down the hall to the bedrooms, and if he noticed she was dragging her heels a bit, he didn't mention it.

"Go get changed," he said, giving her no chance to argue. "I'll meet you on the veranda."

She went, and as she slipped into the already-dry swimsuit, she berated herself for her over-active imagination. Ty hadn't been about to drag her caveman-style into his bedroom and attack her. Even if he was unfathomable sometimes, she at least knew him better than that. Caveman tactics just weren't his style.

Even so, she wrapped the terry-cloth beach jacket snugly around her and tugged the belt tightly, as she pushed open the front screen door and stepped out onto the veranda. Ty moved out of the shadows, saying nothing as he took her hand and led her down the path to the stairs in the reef. Once on the sand, Anne removed her sandals. The fine grains went between her toes as they walked down the beach beyond the line of palm trees.

Under the light of a huge full moon, the cove seemed more isolated than it had during the day. Anne's heartbeat accelerated as Ty became a broad silhouette standing beneath a palm tree, watching while she spread the beach towel. Playing for time, she knelt down to meticulously smooth it, then decided she didn't like it where it was at all. She walked farther down the beach and stopped about ten feet away from the far bordering reef, where she spread the towel again. Then she fidgeted with the plait of her hair until Ty, who had followed, apparently lost patience with her delaying tactics and took control of the situation.

His bronzed skin gleamed in the moonlight as he diminished the distance between them with one long stride. He moved close in front of her and swiftly undid the tie around her waist. Pushing the soft terry fabric from her shoulders and down her arms, he removed the jacket entirely and dropped it onto the towel at their feet. His fingers went up to blaze a trail of fire along her slender neck to the shadowed hollow at the base of her throat and downward to brush slowly across the beginning swell of her breasts, visible above the top of her swimsuit.

"Anne," he murmured, his hands spanning her waist.

His serious, uneven tone indicated he had something much more intimate than swimming in mind, and she intuitively employed playfulness as a line of defense. Laughing softly, she pulled away from him and ran to the water's edge, where the foaming surf sprayed phosphorescent droplets onto the sand. Without looking back, she waded into the sea up to her thighs, cooling her overheated skin in the silky water. Hazarding a glance back over her shoulder, she breathed a sigh of relief when she saw Ty following her into the surf. When she had taken a few more steps, the waves were splashing over her waist. She looked back once more, but Ty had stopped in water that didn't quite reach his knees. Standing very still, he was staring straight ahead, then he turned quickly toward her.

"Anne, come here," he commanded quite sternly, causing the first stirring of apprehension in her.

She hesitated. "But . . ."

"Just come," he repeated tersely, altering her apprehension to fear. When she still didn't move, he reached out one hand to her and said with deliberate calm, "I read recently that sharks often attack in about three feet of water."

With the word shark, she panicked. When he moved toward her, she lunged at him, clutching the hand he held out and nearly catapulting herself against him as he swiftly drew her from the deeper water. Sweeping her up in his strong arms, he carried her back onto the beach, and she clung to his shoulders and buried her face in his neck as a delayed reaction began to make her shake violently.

"You saw something out there!" she squeaked. "Didn't you? Didn't you see something?"

"Not a thing," he replied laconically. "But this little trick always works."

For a moment she was too stunned to speak, but the soft laughter rumbling in his chest confirmed his words. "*Ty!*" she protested, pushing at his shoulders to free herself, but to no avail. "What a terrible thing to do! You nearly scared me to death! Oh, that wasn't fair. It really wasn't. You should be ashamed of yourself."

"Ah, but I'm not," he whispered close to her ear. "If you play games, then I play, too, and that little deception got you right where I want you."

Before she could even begin to protest his statement, he had dropped to his knees on the towel and was tenderly putting her down. His dark eyes swept over the ivory skin that shimmered with a satin-like sheen in the moonglow. Then he was close beside her, one powerful hair-roughened leg pinning both hers beneath its weight. Hearing her startled intake of breath, he cupped her face in both his hands and lowered his dark head.

"Ty," she breathed, but the soft sound was captured by his warm, firm mouth. His lips closed on the lower curve of hers and his strong, even teeth nibbled the softness, sending ripples of ecstasy throughout her body. As the tip of his tongue probed the tender flesh of her inner lip, inflaming her senses, she fought the aching need to yield to him, but lost. Her fingers tangled feverishly in his hair, as the fire he had kindled sent flames dancing over every inch of her skin. A central, aching emptiness made itself known inside her with throbbing insistence. When he turned her to him and his hands curved over her gently rounded hips, pressing her close, her legs tangled with his. She could feel the hardness of his body against her slender thigh, and following a feminine instinct older than time, she rubbed her leg against him, smiling sensuously when a soft groan came from deep in his throat.

Wrapping her arms around his waist, she drew her hands slowly over his broad smooth back, then traced the outline of taut muscles with trembling fingertips.

His lips plundered the soft sweetness of hers, and with each gentle nip of his teeth, she strained closer against him, unable to get near enough. Though their bodies seemed to fit perfectly together, the emptiness within her was becoming all-consuming. His tongue sought the opening flower of her mouth, tasting the honey sweetness within. As his warm, minty breath filled her throat, she was lost in a turmoil of desires that clamored to be fulfilled. With a muffled exclamation, he pressed her slight body down into the towel, and his hand beneath her hips arched her soft warmth upward to meet the dominating iron hardness of his thighs.

Anne was alive with quickening sensations. She explored his shoulders with her lips, touching the tip of her tongue against his heated skin until his hungry mouth sought and took hers again. One lean hand curved over her right hipbone, pressing her down, then spread possessively over her flat abdomen, his fingers brushing the exquisitely sensitive skin of her upper thighs.

When he urgently untied the cords of her swimsuit and peeled the fabric down until her breasts were bared, she moaned softly with the first touch of his fingers on the creamy skin. With the light caress of a gentle breeze, he explored the rounded fullness, making her breathless with waiting, until at last he began to trace circles around the throbbing, swollen peaks. The rough edge of his thumbs brushed over the roseate crests, and when they hardened beneath his touch, he tasted first one, then the other, grazing his tongue over each in turn.

Fire surged through her body, and she made a soft, tremulous sound of delight as his hand slipped beneath the swimsuit to stroke the satiny skin of her abdomen, but as his fingers moved lower, she tensed instinctively.

"Anne, love," he whispered coaxingly, his lips playing with her own. "Try to relax. I want you so badly and you want me. We don't need to wait any longer."

She wasn't his love, but at that moment, it didn't matter. All that mattered was giving her love to him. Unable to answer him in words, she responded by urging his mouth down to hers again.

"I won't rush you, I promise," he muttered, bringing both hands up to cup her face as hers cupped his. The planes of his lean face hardened beneath her fingertips as he tempered a long, arousing kiss with exquisite tenderness.

But even as she breathed a shuddering sigh that signaled total surrender, the moment was shattered by the sound of voices and laughter farther along the beach.

In the shadow of the reef, Ty and Anne weren't visible. As Ty tensed at the sound of the intruders and cursed beneath his breath, Anne peered over his left shoulder and saw at least ten people milling around near the first in the line of palm trees. When she recognized Jenny as one of them, she hastily pulled away from Ty and rearranged her swimsuit. "It's Jenny, Mike and Rob, I guess," she told him. "Looks like they and some of their friends are gathering driftwood to build a fire."

"What terrific timing they have," Ty muttered grumpily, but when she smiled, a smile hovered on his firmly carved lips, too. Taking her small face between his hands, he gazed intently at her as his thumbs stroked the delicate arches of her brows. "I wish they hadn't come, Anne, but it won't happen this way again. There must be some private place on St. Croix, and I intend to find it and take you there tomorrow night . . . if you're willing to go."

As he stood and pulled her up beside him, she was suddenly too shy to meet his eyes, but she nodded. She knew then that she would go with him tomorrow night. She loved him, and even knowing there were women like Millicent Beaumont in his life, she would go with him anywhere, anytime.

Chapter Nine

Saturday evening Anne sat at the dressing table, brushing her freshly washed hair. In the warm lamplight, the golden strands shimmered with every move of her head, and the sun-streaked healthy sheen didn't diminish, even as she quickly wove a plait and pinned it into a chignon on her nape. That persistently wayward tendril sprang loose and brushed her cheek, but tonight she didn't really care if it did. Leaning toward the mirror, she examined her complexion, flawless except for a sparse scattering of freckles. An excited sparkle glowed in her gray eyes. Heightened color tinted her cheeks and a secretive smile curved her lips, as she turned to watch Jenny leave the adjoining bathroom, a towel wrapped around her head.

Pausing to secure the tie of her bathrobe, the younger girl eyed Anne speculatively for a moment, then snapped her fingers. "Hey, would you do me a favor? After I blow dry my hair, will you help me put it up the way you have yours? I'm tired of this mop of mine hanging down my back all the time—makes me look too young. I'm sure I'd look much more mature if I put mine up, too."

With a slight toss of one hand, Anne nodded. "Sure I'll help you put it up, if that's really what you want. But I have to tell you that I think your hair is very beautiful hanging free down your back."

Jenny grimaced. "It might look beautiful for a little girl, but I'm seventeen. I think it's time to change my image." Scooting across the room, she rummaged through her unpacked suitcase, then dragged out a small hair dryer. Scanning the walls of the room for an electrical outlet, she added in an offhanded manner, "You sure do look all aglow tonight. Any special reason? Are Bob and Meg Peterson planning some big treat or something?"

"Actually, Ty and I won't be with Mr. and Mrs. Peterson tonight," Anne answered, adjusting the lapels of the royal blue kimono she was wearing. "They had already accepted an invitation to a party for tonight before Ty decided to come here, so he insisted they go. He's just taking me out to dinner."

Jenny nodded absently, as if she saw nothing unusual in those plans. Then, spying an outlet on the opposite wall, she went to plug in the dryer cord. "Mind if I sit on your bed while I dry my hair?" she asked, even as she flopped down on it and began to unwind the towel covering her head. "I hope this mess gets dry fast. Rob wants me to be ready by seven. He's taking Mike and me to a new disco near Frederiksted."

Standing, Anne smoothed the kimono down over her gently rounded hips. "You know, I think you're really having fun here. I'm glad you came."

"Oh, me too," the younger girl agreed with a careless toss of one hand. "I never guessed how much fun I'd have with Rob and Mike. They can both be so zany."

Wisely, Anne didn't mention Kirt Callen, and as the hair dryer suddenly came on with a roar, she could only hope that this pleasant weekend had helped Ty's sister to see that young men nearer her own age were much more suitable companions for her than Kirt could ever be.

Glancing at the wristwatch she had put on the dressing table, Anne found that it was only six-thirty. Another whole hour had to pass before she and Ty were to leave for the restaurant, and she was beginning to feel less than calm. Though she had spent most of the day with Ty, he had never mentioned what his after-dinner plans included, but she had been unable to forget what he had said last night on the beach. His promise to find some private place where they could be alone together this evening had been foremost in her thoughts all day. And now with the evening almost upon her, she wondered if she had been insane to agree to go to such a place with him. A few short weeks ago, she would never have considered planning such an irrevocable step, but now her feelings for Ty superseded all her innate caution. More than anything in the world, she wanted to be alone with him.

It was too early to dress. Yet, Anne couldn't sit still. After glancing at Jenny who was humming loudly to herself and staring out the window as she dried her hair, Anne tugged the kimono more snugly about her and secured the tie belt, then left the bedroom. Directly across the hall, Ty's door was closed, but hearing his shower running, Anne knew she should be in no hurry to get ready. All she had to do was slip into her dress and shoes anyway.

The gleaming parquet floor of the great room was cool beneath her bare feet, as she passed through and stepped out onto the veranda. The early evening air was filled with the perfume of countless flowers, which she inhaled appreciatively. Leaning on the railing, she gazed up at the bowl of blue sky tinted in the west by the orange hue of the setting sun. There was a peaceful silence over the lush exotic greenery that was broken only by the rhythmic breaking of waves on the reef. With grating abruptness, however, the quiet was shattered by the jangling ring of the phone. Simply to stop the intrusive noise, Anne rushed into the great room to pick up the receiver and was immediately assaulted by a strident feminine voice.

"I want to speak to Ty," the woman demanded.

"He's unable to come to the phone right now," Anne replied. "Could I give him a message?"

"Yes. No! Just get him and bring him to the phone," the woman commanded rather frantically. "I'm sure he'll come if you tell him it's Millicent calling."

Anne's heart sank, and her stomach tightened so painfully that she almost felt nauseous. She glanced down the hall toward Ty's room, and for a fleeting instant she was tempted to tell Millicent he wasn't there. Yet, an inherent honestly prevented her from uttering the lie. After taking a deep breath, she spoke into the phone. "Hold on please. I'll tell him you wish to speak with him."

"But wait," Millicent called before Anne could put down the receiver. "Tell him that I'm here on St. Croix at Daddy's beach house."

Anne's shoulders drooped slightly as she agreed to do that, but she resolutely squared them again as she walked to Ty's room. When she knocked lightly, he answered almost immediately, too disturbingly attractive in a short white terry bathrobe, tied loosely around his trim waist. His initial smile faded when she didn't return it.

"Millicent Beaumont is on the phone," Anne announced in her most prim businesslike voice. "She wanted me to tell you that she is here on St. Croix at her father's beach house."

"Millicent's here?" Ty muttered, raking his fingers through hair still damp from his shower. Then without another word and only a brooding glance at Anne, he stepped out of his room and strode down the hall.

An ever-increasing constriction in Anne's throat made it difficult to swallow, as she walked back into her own bedroom.

"Hey, my hair'll be dry in a minute or two," Jenny yelled over the roar of the dryer. "Then you can help me put it up, okay?"

Nodding, Anne sank down on the red velvet cushion of the dressing table chair. Her gaze involuntarily sought her best black dress hanging in the open closet across from her. Now there was a very real possibility that she wouldn't be wearing anything besides her kimono, because she might not be going anywhere.

"It's all dry," Jenny declared, disturbing Anne's reverie.

Desperately, Anne tried to keep her mind a blank as she gently ran a brush through Jenny's silken tresses. She was having very little luck in that endeavor, when Ty knocked on the door, then stepped into the room.

Almost of their own volition, her eyes met his. But if there was a message in those dark blue depths, it was beyond her at the moment to decipher it. He had dressed, although it wasn't even seven o'clock. Anne supposed that meant he was planning to leave before then. And she was right.

"I'm sorry, Anne, but Millicent's upset and wants to see me," he said regretfully. "I think I should go."

"But what about Anne?" Jenny spoke up, her tone accusing. "You were supposed to take her out to dinner. What's she going to do now that you aren't going to?"

"I'm still taking you out to dinner," he told Anne, ignoring his sister. His darkening gaze traveled slowly over the curves faintly outlined against the satin-like fabric of the kimono. "Go ahead and get ready. I'll be back here by seven-thirty, I promise."

The barely perceptible uptilting of Anne's small chin hinted at her strong sense of pride. She simply stared at him, not believing for a second that he would be back in time to take her to dinner. Apparently her doubt wasn't lost on him.

His jaw hardened. "I will be back, Anne, so be ready to go when I get here."

Her eyes flashed fiery defiance at his commanding tone, but before she could make a biting retort, he turned and left the room.

"Old Millie sure is chasing him down," Jenny remarked, totally unaware of Anne's tension. "And it looks as if she's about to catch him, too. I guess Mother will be ecstatic about it if she does. She always thought they were perfect for each other and was very upset when Millicent married someone else."

"She's still married, didn't you say?" Anne asked as nonchalantly as possible as she divided the younger girl's hair into three equal sections. "Isn't it possible she'll go back to her husband?"

"Oh, I doubt that. They're separated now and everybody says that marriage was doomed from the start. They just weren't compatible." Jenny made a little moue with her mouth. "You see, he's a captain in the Navy or the Merchant Marines or something like that, so he doesn't make a lot of money. And he didn't come from the same social background as Millicent did. Her father's one of the wealthiest men in Alexandria, but her husband's family's just . . ."

"Average? Like mine," Anne murmured, but smiled slightly at Jenny in the mirror, knowing she wasn't being deliberately snobbish. She was only repeating a philosophy she had heard all her life, and Anne couldn't fault her for that. Though her fingers were trembling, she quickly braided the three thick sections of Jenny's hair into a smooth plait. After making certain there was some fullness in the soft waves edging Jenny's face, she wound the braid into a chignon and pinned it securely. Noticing the pure white camellia in the vase on the dressing table, she impulsively took it out and broke off part of the stem. The edge of her teeth pressed down into her soft lower lip as she gazed at the rose-like flower. Ty had picked it for her that afternoon, asking her to wear it tonight, but now she wouldn't be needing it.

"Here, this will look nice tucked over one ear," she told Jenny. "The white is just right for your dark hair."

Jenny's eyes sparkled with enthusiasm as Anne pinned the flower above her left ear. "My, that does look pretty, doesn't it? I really like my hair up like this. Thanks for doing it."

"Any time," Anne said softly, leaving the dressing table to go sit in the overstuffed armchair by the far window. Closing her eyes, she rested her head against the cushion and tucked her bare feet up beside her.

"Why are you sitting down?" Jenny asked. "It's already after seven, in case you didn't know it. Aren't you going to get ready as Ty told you to?"

A slight smile trembled on Anne's lips as she reopened her eyes. "I don't really think I should waste my time, do you?"

Jenny grimaced. "Well, maybe not. Knowing Millicent, she'll hold onto him most of the night, now that she's snared him." She spread her arms in an expressive gesture. "But you can't just stay here by yourself. Bob and Meg are going to a party, you said, so they won't even be home for dinner. Where will you eat?"

"I'm not really very hungry," Anne admitted truthfully, though she tried not to sound too bleak. "And I'll be just fine here by myself. I have a book to read."

"Read! On our last night in St. Croix! You're crazy," Jenny declared, shaking her head. "No, I won't let you spend the evening like that. Get dressed and you can go to the disco with the guys and me."

Though Anne appreciated the offer, the thought of going to a disco simply didn't appeal. Still, she didn't want to tell Jenny that. "Thanks for asking, but you're already late getting ready. If you wait for me to get dressed, you'll be even later and Rob and Mike might get impatient."

"So, let them. Waiting won't kill them."

"No, really, I'll just stay here."

"Oh Anne, please come. I'll feel so bad if you don't come with us," Jenny said beseechingly, proving she could feel concern for someone other than herself. "Why should you have to spend your last night on the island all alone?"

Why indeed? Anne pondered, a sudden resolve stiffening her shoulders. Why should she sit there by herself all evening while Ty was having a high old time somewhere with Millicent Beaumont? She shouldn't, she decided. She wouldn't give him the satisfaction of knowing she had waited for him all alone. Besides, she wasn't certain she could cope with the loneliness she was now feeling, a loneliness more intense than any she had ever known. At least if she went out with Jenny and the guys, she would have the comfort of human companionship.

Rising swiftly to her feet, she nodded. "All right,

you've talked me into it, thank goodness. I will go." As Jenny grinned, Anne hurried to the closet. "While I'm dressing, why don't you walk over to the main house and tell Rob and Mike I'll be there in a jiffy. That is, if they don't mind having me tag along."

Catching up her purse, Jenny laughed on her way to the door. "I'm sure they won't mind one little bit. In fact, Rob may just whoop for joy when he hears."

After the younger girl disappeared down the hall, Anne slipped on the black dress and stepped into black narrow-strapped high heels. "This whole mess is your own fault," she muttered aloud to herself while picking up her purse. "You were the one who made the stupid mistake of falling in love with your boss. And this time, it's going to be impossible to forget the man."

According to the clock in the great room, it was after seven-thirty when Anne started to leave. She smiled rather sadly. Ty was supposed to have returned five minutes before, but, of course, he hadn't. She realized then that she had still held some hope he would. "Gullible little ninny," she called herself. Lifting her chin slightly, she stepped out onto the veranda, but before she could pull the wooden door closed behind her, the telephone began to ring. She hesitated only a second, then shut the door firmly, deciding she would spare Ty from having to lie about why he wasn't coming back. And the sound of the phone still ringing brought a smile of grim satisfaction to her mouth as the screen door slammed shut behind her with a resounding bang, and she ran lightly down the veranda steps.

Anne made an all-out effort at gaiety throughout what seemed an endless evening. By eleven-thirty, however, her cheeks were aching from the smile she had maintained for hours, and she was weary of acting as if she felt lighthearted and happy. Rob, Mike and

Jenny were pleasant companions, but at this particular time, Anne couldn't fully appreciate their frivolous banter. Even the drink she'd had, made her feel worse instead of better. It had induced in her a nearly overwhelming desire to cry. Now, with the pressure of unshed tears behind her eyes, she was getting a miserable headache. Mere companionship wasn't compensation for the loss she felt, and she realized she really needed to be alone. She longed for someone to suggest that they return to the bungalow but, unfortunately, it didn't quite work out that way.

"I have a terrific idea," Rob announced loudly, trying to be heard over the sultry beat of the steel band. "Let's really make a night of it, okay? After a disco and a nightclub featuring the best steel band on the island, what could be better than a party? My friend Julie Thorpe's having one tonight, so why don't we go?"

Though Jenny and Mike chimed in to voice their approval of his suggestion, Anne had to demur. Massaging her temples with her fingertips, she shook her head. "I'm sorry, but I'm getting a terrible headache. I don't think I'm up to a party. Why don't you drop me off at the bungalow, and then you can go on without me."

At first, the other three insisted they couldn't just take her home and leave her if she wasn't feeling well, but finally she managed to convince them that she needed solitude and absolute quiet. Only sleep would rid her of the headache she had. They drove her back to the Peterson estate immediately.

"You needn't get out," she told them while alighting from Rob's car in front of his parents' house. "Just go on to the party and have fun. I'll be fine here. I plan to take a couple of aspirin and go straight to bed."

"But I'm walking you to the bungalow," Mike insisted gallantly, unwilling to hear any argument from her. And after she had said goodnight to Rob and Jenny, he took her hand as they walked around the Peterson house to the flagstone path that led to the guest cottage. Once there, he brushed a kiss across her cheek. "Hope your headache's gone soon, honey," he murmured. Then he waited until she had ascended the veranda stairs before he turned to walk back to the car.

With a deep, heartfelt sigh, Anne opened the door of the bungalow and stepped into the great room. Moonlight filtering in through the windows provided enough illumination for her to see where she was going, so she didn't bother to switch on the overhead light. That was a decision she regretted almost immediately. As she walked across the room toward the hallway, there was a sudden rustle of sound and a dark form rose from the shadowy sofa.

Anne's heart leaped up in her throat, and she uttered a startled cry as she recognized the looming form as a man. Immediately, she feared she had surprised an intruder. As the menacing form advanced on her stealthily, she took several jerky steps backward and looked around frantically for some avenue of escape. Deciding she must try to find refuge in one of the bedrooms, she spun around and sprinted down the hallway, but she didn't get far before her right wrist was captured in a vise-like grip.

"*Where* have you been?" a deep voice demanded to know.

Anne released her breath in a gasp of relief and peered up into the darkness. That deep voice was Ty's and now, up close to him, she was able to recognize his face. Yet, that first surge of sheer panic had left her too overwrought to speak, so she could only stare mutely up at him.

"I asked you where you've been," he at last repeated tersely. "And I want an answer fast."

Still too confused to think clearly, Anne said simply, "I went out."

"Don't try to play games with me, Anne," he nearly growled at her, hard hands clamping around her waist. "I know you went out, and I know you went with Mike."

"And Rob and Jenny."

"Really? Then where were they a minute ago when you and Mike were outside kissing each other?"

"I wasn't kissing him! *He* kissed *me.*"

"What's the difference?" Ty retorted, his voice ominously low. "I certainly didn't see you resist his kiss."

"Well, what was I supposed to do?" Anne countered sarcastically. "Knock him down with a karate chop to his neck or something? He wasn't committing a crime, you know. He was only giving me a friendly kiss. Now, I'd appreciate it if you'd let me go. I have a headache and I want to go to bed."

"Oh no, Anne, you're not going anywhere just yet." Ty's grip on her tightened and he shook her slightly. "First you're going to tell me why you went out at all, when I told you I'd return at seven-thirty."

Anne tensed with anger. He had some nerve, getting angry with her for finding some way to pass the long hours while he played around with his old girlfriend! Suddenly, her palm itched to connect with his lean brown face. But her anger vanished almost as quickly as it had come and left only disillusionment and pain in its place.

"I went out because I had to eat dinner somewhere, didn't I?" she muttered. "And since I knew you weren't coming back . . ."

"Come on, Anne, you can think of a better lie than

that," he whispered harshly. "You knew I was coming back. I promised I would, didn't I?"

"Yes, but promises aren't always kept."

"Mine are. And you would know that if you'd bothered to wait around here until I could return. But you weren't willing to do that, were you?" he asked grimly, lean fingers pressing into her flesh. "You were already gone when I tried to call here about seven-thirty to tell you I'd be a little later than I'd planned. Unfortunately for me, I imagined you didn't answer the phone because you were taking a walk outside, so I rushed back here at eight o'clock."

"I'll just bet," Anne snapped. In the darkened hall, she was unable to see the grim thinning of his firmly shaped lips, so she couldn't heed the warning his taut expression conveyed. Her words tumbled out recklessly. "What do you think I am? Some kind of gullible little nitwit? You can't really expect me to believe you returned here at eight o'clock! I'm not that stupid, I'll have you know. I don't imagine for one moment that you'd been in this bungalow more than a few minutes before Mike brought me back."

Uttering a muffled imprecation, Ty thrust her into his bedroom and switched on the light, his eyes blazing furiously as he glared down at her. "And just what is that supposed to mean?" he muttered, his low tone intimidating. "Are you accusing me of lying? If you are, I want to know why. I've never lied to you before, have I? Why should I start now?"

She thrust out her chin defiantly as her answer came out in a rush of words. "Maybe you hope a lie will ease your conscience about standing me up tonight!"

Ty was perfectly still for a fraction of a second, as his narrowed gaze flicked over her. Then suddenly a glimmer of understanding warmed his icy blue eyes, and his strongly carved features gentled. His hold on her waist loosened slightly, and when he shook her again, there was more tenderness than anger in the action. "Is that what this is all about, Anne?" he asked softly. "Are you upset because I had to go see Millicent?"

"I'm not upset at all. I . . ."

"Yes, you are. I can see it now," he interrupted gently, then shook his head. "But you shouldn't be upset, Anne. I can explain about Millicent."

"You don't owe me an explanation, Mr. Manning," Anne replied coolly, though her eyes were a stormy gray. "What you and Millicent do is no concern of mine. Your private life is none of my business. Now, if you'll excuse me, I'd like to go to bed. It's late."

"I don't excuse you," Ty said, his voice still low, but conveying a hint of impatience again. "You're not going to bed until we've straightened out this misunderstanding. Is that clear?"

Anne couldn't stand much more of his baiting. The storm in her eyes was threatening to produce a veritable deluge of tears, and she had far too much pride to cry in front of him. She had to get away. Clamping her fingers around his large wrists, she tried to push his hands away. When he wouldn't release her, she exploded. "Take your hands off me!" she cried sharply, then drew in a swift startled breath at his reaction. She had never seen him so angry, not even with Jenny, who could sometimes try the patience of a saint. His eyes glittered like sapphires, and a muscle ticked forebodingly in his clenched jaw. Too late she realized his superior physical strength gave him an innate power over her that she couldn't hope to fight. She began to struggle. "Ty, please, I'm . . ."

"Don't push me too far, Anne," he warned, resolutely drawing her close to him, so close that his muscular thighs pressed hard on hers. "After making me sit here and wait for you for hours, I think you owe me something. And I'm about to collect."

"Don't! Ty!" she gasped, as he lowered his head. Wrenching free with a soft cry of fear, she sped toward the door but never got there. Cruel fingers clamped her waist, and Ty jerked her into enfolding arms that tightened with iron hardness around her.

"You won't escape this time," he promised gruffly. "I want you. You can either give me what I want, or I'll just take it. My patience's all gone, Anne. You've kept me waiting too long already."

"Please, Ty!" she begged, as his lips grazed the delicate line of her jaw, then sought her own. His ravishing mouth ruthlessly possessed hers and she began to struggle desperately. But she wasn't a person disposed to violence, and since she couldn't force herself to bite or scratch or kick, he easily overcame her resistance. Had he continued to be brutal, she could have gone on struggling, but, as it was, the sudden gentling of his embrace and the tender persuasion of his hard lips on hers annihilated the defenses she might have built up against him. Her slight body arched traitorously against the long length of his, and as he whispered her name and gathered her closer still, her bare arms slipped up to encircle his neck. Millicent ceased to exist, as his kiss deepened to an almost intimate exploration. His lips were demandingly hungry as they captured and possessed the soft tender shape of hers. His tongue invaded her mouth.

Though Anne never wanted him to stop kissing her, she trembled as he pulled the pins from her hair, then threaded his fingers through the loose braid, separating the silken strands. Winding the golden swathe round one hand, he tilted her head back and trailed hot, seeking kisses down her creamy neck and along the skin that stretched tautly over her collarbone. Sparkles of delight danced over her skin as his mouth explored her.

"Anne, you smell delicious," he muttered huskily, nibbling the rounded curve of her shoulder with his teeth and running the tip of his tongue over the delicate contours. "You taste delicious."

"Kiss me," she breathed, urging his mouth back up to hers. When his lips took hers with marauding swiftness, she moaned softly at the pleasure his possessive touch evoked. Even when he lowered the back zipper of her dress and pushed the straps off her shoulders and down her arms, she made no effort to resist. She only shivered slightly when cool air caressed her skin as the dress slipped to her feet with a soft, rustling sound. Ty held her from him, his eyes alight with desire as his gaze drifted slowly over her slender young body, clad only in a half-slip and a strapless lace bra.

"Anne, you're lovely," he whispered hoarsely. His teeth nipped the tender lobe of one ear, as his hands molded her hips and brought her firmly against his hardening thighs. The hot, demanding pressure of aroused masculinity seemed to burn her skin through the thin nylon of her slip, and her legs weakened beneath her. Sensing a nearly intolerable desire in him, she was suddenly half afraid.

"Ty, I can't," she whispered breathlessly against the strong brown column of his neck. "I want to, but I . . . can't."

"It's too late to say no now," he whispered back, relentless hands roving over her with sweetly persuasive gentleness.

As he reached out and switched off the light, then

swept her up into his arms to carry her to his bed, she was overcome by the dizzying sensation of anticipation mingling with fear. She could only cling weakly to his broad shoulders as he pulled back the coverlet and put her down on the bed. As he slipped his arms from beneath her, he released the catch of her bra. With evocative slowness, he drew the sheer wisp of lace away from her skin. In the soft moonlight that streamed through his window and across the bed, she watched with half-closed eyes while mahogany-dark hands cupped the ivory fullness of her breasts. Fever seemed to consume her body and the central throbbing ache within her peaked to a pulsing emptiness that only he could assuage. Yet, as he straightened to pull his cream-colored sweater off over his head and she saw the powerful rippling of muscles beneath his bronze skin, she uttered a little cry and turned over to press her face into the pillow.

Tears filled her eyes as the insanity of what was happening washed over her again. He didn't love her, so she shouldn't surrender herself to him. She would be courting disaster if she did. Her relationship with him was not a casual thing to her. In the past few weeks, her love for him had deepened and strengthened to such an extent that she knew she couldn't become intimately involved with him, then shrug off her feelings and forget him when he tired of her later.

She tensed as she felt Ty lower himself onto the bed beside her, and she trembled violently as he threaded his fingers through her tousled hair. She couldn't suppress a soft half-sob.

"Anne, don't cry," he coaxed, stroking her hair, then massaging the tensed muscles of her bare shoulders. "I don't want you to be afraid of me, and I don't think you really are, are you?"

She shook her head, knowing in that instant that it was actually herself she feared. Slowly she began to relax beneath his caressing hands, as they moved expertly over her back, massaging, stroking, gently demanding the release of her tension. Lean fingers probed the delicate structure of her spine, sending tremors of sensual delight throughout her body. As his lips began to follow the path his fingers had blazed, fire surged through her veins. And, as his mouth sought the insweeping arch between narrow waist and gently sloping hips, she forgot everything except the need to be closer to him.

Turning over, she clasped her arms around his neck, and her lips sought the hard delight of his. The weight of his lean body pressed her down into the softness of the mattress, and the kisses they exchanged lengthened and deepened to the dangerous prelude to her surrender. The lissome, naked strength of his body enveloped her in warmth beneath him. Anne became intoxicated by the wholly masculine scent and feel of him. Her small hands shook slightly as they ran over his broad back, down to lightly touch his lean bare hips.

With a soft groan, he arched her to him, removing her slip. And then there was only one remaining barrier between them. Yet, he didn't immediately remove that last barrier. As if he meant to reassure her, he cupped her face in both hands. His firm mouth covered hers and moved lazily until her desire was aroused to a fever pitch. And when he started to slip his fingertips beneath the waistband of her panties, she didn't tense but breathed a tremulous sigh of sweet acquiescence.

The hardening response of Ty's lips was echoed throughout the length of his body. But before another second could pass, there was a loud thump outside the bungalow.

"What was that?" Anne breathed.

"Maybe a tree branch falling in the forest. I don't know," he muttered unevenly. "Anne, don't go all tense on me now, please."

She didn't want to be tense, but the unexpected noise had suddenly brought an unbidden thought to her mind, a thought she had to share with him. "But Ty, what if that was Jenny?" she whispered urgently. "She could be back any time and . . ."

Muttering beneath his breath, Ty turned over onto his back, resting one forearm across his eyes. "Blast it, Anne, must you always be so efficient? Why did you have to remember Jenny at such an inopportune moment?"

His tone was not teasing and Anne wished, too, that she didn't have such an efficient memory. "I'm sorry, Ty," she said softly, brushing her hand across his hair-roughened chest.

Hard fingers stilled hers and he put her hand away from him. "Go to your room, Anne. Or, Jenny or no Jenny, I'm going to make love to you. Put on my robe and get into your own bed before I decide to keep you in mine."

She didn't argue with him. That low, deceptively calm tone of voice always meant he was serious. Lowering her feet to the floor, she reached for the terry robe he had left on the back of the chair by the bed. After wrapping it tightly around her, she hurried out, not daring to say another word to him.

Five minutes later she was glad she had left him, though she hadn't wanted to. As she switched out the light in her room, then slipped between the cool sheets, the sound of Jenny's voice drifted in from the veranda. A minute or so later, when the younger girl tiptoed into the bedroom, Anne pretended not to be awake. Actually, however, sleep was a long time coming. She spent long hours gazing up at the moonlight-dappled ceiling, wondering how it would have been if she could have given herself completely to Ty tonight. If they hadn't had Jenny to consider, she could have still been there with him, in his bed, in his arms, close to him.

Chapter Ten

In the office Friday morning after the St. Croix trip, Anne sat strumming her fingers on her desk, deep in thought. She was finding Jenny's behavior particularly baffling. Since they had returned to Alexandria Sunday evening, the younger girl had reverted to her former rebelliousness, though on St. Croix she had seemed so happy at times. Anne couldn't understand the difference in her. Still worse, Anne was relatively certain that Kirt Callen had resumed his phone calls to Jenny. Anne didn't look forward to telling Ty about that, but knew she had to. She would tell him this morning and get it over with, she decided, as she picked up a couple of sharpened pencils and a steno pad in preparation for the morning's routine dictation.

Before Anne could leave her desk to go to Ty, however, the door of her office opened and Millicent Beaumont sauntered in, meticulously chic as always, wearing a sand-colored designer suit and a red silk blouse. Fashionably thin, she was perfection plus from the top of her expertly coiffed hair to the tips of her snakeskin pumps. Actually, she was nearly too perfect, looking as if she had just stepped from a page in a fashion magazine, Anne thought rather uncharitably. All the same, she gave Millicent a polite smile as the willowly woman struck an insouciant pose in front of her desk.

"Hello, Miss Fairfax," Millicent drawled, tucking her snakeskin clutch purse beneath her arm as she gave a trained smile that never reached her eyes. "I've missed seeing you at the restaurant lately, but I suppose you don't miss being a waitress, do you? Such a boring occupation, I should imagine."

Anne refrained from answering. "May I help you, Mrs. Beaumont?" she asked instead.

"Oh, I stopped by to see Ty, that's all." With a lazily limp toss of her hand, Millicent gestured toward the door. "I'll just go on in."

"I'll just buzz him first," Anne said flatly, but before she could press the button on the intercom, Millicent was ambling toward the double doors.

"Never mind, dear," she said condescendingly. "When I saw Ty last night, he asked me to stop by this morning. He's expecting my visit."

Anne breathed a disillusioned sigh as the older woman proceeded into Ty's office without even knocking. Pressing her fingertips against her forehead, Anne sat back in her chair. So Ty had been with Millicent last night. She had wondered if that might be the case, but since he hadn't mentioned where he was going, she had hoped he was seeing someone else, a business acquaintance perhaps.

"Dreamer," she called herself now, staring bleakly out the wide window at the high-rise office building across the street. Even after that episode with Ty in his bedroom at the bungalow Saturday night, she had known she was fooling herself when she tried to believe she really meant anything to him. Millicent was the one he loved.

She sat up straight in her chair, stiffening her spine with sudden resolve. Somehow, she was going to regain control of her life, and she planned to begin by treating Ty in a purely businesslike manner. It wouldn't be easy, but if she really tried, perhaps she could even suppress the love she felt for him. Perhaps she could, but she seriously doubted it. Yet, even if she was destined to always love him, that didn't mean she had to let him use her. He might be willing to indulge in a casual affair, but she wasn't. She had some pride left, and his involvement with Millicent Beaumont hurt her too much for her to pretend it didn't exist.

For once, Anne was too lost in thoughts about her personal life to keep her mind on office duties. It came as something of a surprise to realize that an entire half hour had passed, when Millicent came strolling out of Ty's office. Ty accompanied her, and though Anne pretended to be busy with some papers on her desk and tried not to watch them together, it was difficult to ignore Millicent's possessive behavior. Leaning her svelte body against him, she draped her long arms around his neck and kissed him lingeringly on the mouth. "I hope I didn't keep you from your work too long, darling," she cooed, "but I did want to tell you how much last night meant to me."

As Ty simply nodded discreetly, Anne felt as if someone had delivered a blow to her chest, though she showed no outward evidence of her distress. Her expression remained placid as she rummaged through the bottom drawer of her desk, trying to appear as if she hadn't even heard Millicent's comment.

At last the other woman swept regally out of the

room. Sensing that Ty was watching her, Anne glanced up. Unable to meet his eyes directly, she held up the steno pad expectantly. "Are you ready for me?" When he said that he was, she immediately followed him into his office. To her dismay, he didn't go around the desk to sit behind it. Instead, he leaned back against it, very close to her chair, his long legs outstretched to support him and his feet nearly touching hers.

Detecting the clean masculine scent of his after-shave, Anne felt an abrupt and nearly overpowering need to touch him. It would have been so temporarily gratifying and so easy. All she needed to do was reach out and brush her fingertips over the large tan hand curved around the edge of the desk. Yet, she managed to overcome the temptation to do that and berated herself mentally for even feeling tempted.

Throughout the remainder of the letter-taking session, Anne never once looked up at him. There was something comforting in the mechanics of shorthand. She only had to deal with the deep sound of his voice as he dictated the words. Her hand skimmed swiftly across the paper, ciphering those words into symbols. But when the dictation of all the letters was finished, she felt vulnerable again, as if the steno pad had been a shield that she could no longer hide behind. Now, she had to involve herself in his personal life again. She had to tell him about Jenny.

After closing the steno pad and tucking one of the pencils into the spiral cylinder at the top, she unnecessarily smoothed her navy linen skirt and took a deep breath. "I have to tell you some unpleasant news," she announced softly, staring at his feet. "It's about Jenny. I'm fairly sure she's still in contact with Kirt Callen."

"I thought maybe she was beginning to be sensible about him," Ty said, his low, clipped tone conveying disapproval and more than a little irritation. "But I guess that was wishful thinking on my part. I suppose you mean she's seen him since we returned from St. Croix?"

"I don't know if she's actually seen him or not," Anne gestured uncertainly. "I only know that she was very secretive about a call she got last night. We were in the study together, and she answered the phone when it rang. She hardly said anything to the caller, asking him to hold on while she went up to her room to take the call on her phone there. She wanted me to hang up the study phone for her after she'd had time to get upstairs. When I did, I heard a man's voice, and I'm pretty certain it was Kirt's."

Ty nodded. "I see. You know, I'm about to decide to have a nice long talk with Kirt. This whole business is beginning to annoy me immensely."

"There's only one problem with that. Kirt Callen would be quite capable of telling Jenny that you were trying to keep them apart. I really believe that would only make her more determined to talk to him, maybe even start seeing him more often, and that's the last thing in the world we want to happen. I'll try having another talk with her tonight, but I don't know how much good it will do."

"If I can't talk to him and we can't reason with her, what do you suggest we do?"

"I'm not sure there's anything we can do," Anne replied with a sigh. "Except hope Jenny will begin to tire of this silly game of defiance she's playing and will forget about Kirt. If only she would . . . I can't bear to think of that cad using her, then tossing her aside when another young girl comes along. Something like that shouldn't happen to Jenny. I hate to think of the emotional damage that might do to her."

"So do I," Ty murmured, his eyes narrowing as he

gazed down at her. "You really care about Jenny, don't you?"

The sudden gentling of his expression and the warmth that appeared in his eyes had a disturbing effect on Anne's senses. Shifting restlessly, she stared down at her hands to avoid looking at him. "Of course, I care about her," she answered softly at last. "She's really a sweet girl, just a little confused right now. I only wish I could help her."

"But I think you have helped, Anne," Ty told her, reaching down and taking one small hand to draw her up to stand before him. "Jenny's already less hostile than she was before you came to live with us."

"You're very kind," Anne said almost inaudibly, staring glumly at the long fingers that were brushing slowly over the back of her hand. His touch was evoking sensations that she was now too afraid to enjoy. Since she had decided a mere physical relationship with him would never be enough for her, she knew she would have to deny herself the luxury of being close to him. And she had to start now. Yet, she felt an excruciating sense of loss as she gently, but determinedly, extracted her hand from his.

Ty's dark brows lifted questioningly and he stood up straight, then stepped closer to her. As he caressed her smooth cheek with the back of his hand, she took a jerky step backward away from him, murmuring a soft protest. He scowled, "What's wrong, Anne?"

"Nothing's wrong, exactly," she replied, her voice embarrassingly strained. She looked everywhere except directly at him, then raised her shoulders and let them fall in a tired shrug. "It's just that . . . well, I . . . don't think you should touch me . . . that way anymore."

"You can't be serious?" he asked roughly, and when

she nodded, his hands descended onto her shoulders. "I can't believe you mean that."

She nodded again. "But I do."

His grip on her shoulders tightened almost painfully. "Then may I ask what has made you decide you don't want me to touch you?"

"I just think it would be best if you didn't," she said, almost in a whisper. "You remember I told you I thought it was wrong for a secretary to become involved with her boss. It's just not a good idea. Our relationship seemed to get out of control, and now I think it's time we try to get it back to the way it was at first. You know, strictly business."

"Sticking strictly to business might be possible for computerized robots, Anne," he said tautly. "But we happen to be people, and we're attracted to each other."

"We shouldn't be."

"So, we won't be? Is that what you're saying? Well, I'm sorry, Anne, but life's not that simple. Some human responses and emotions can't be controlled so easily."

"Well, I intend to try to control mine," she muttered, managing to get the words past that hard knot in her throat. "I promised myself I wouldn't get involved with you, and I have to keep that promise."

"And what good does that promise do you when I kiss you?" he asked rather impatiently, hauling her to him, covering her mouth with the warm, seeking firmness of his.

Anne's lips parted traitorously, and she responded to his kiss with an urgency that equaled his, but only for an instant. Then the memory of Millicent kissing him good-bye this morning came unbidden to her mind, and she pushed away from him to gasp softly, "Don't! Please. I don't want you to do that again."

The anger her words provoked in him seemed almost a tangible thing between them, and Anne's breath caught as Ty grasped her chin in one hand and tilted her head back, forcing her to look directly at him. "I'm disappointed in you," he announced bluntly, blue fire flashing in his eyes. "Are you sure this is really the way you want it to be?"

"Yes," she lied, her voice choked. "I'm . . . sure."

A mocking smile played over his firmly carved mouth. "Then that's the way it will be. I've never forced myself on any woman, and I'm not going to start with you. But, tell me something, Anne. When are you going to stop being afraid to live?"

The sarcasm conveyed by his low mocking tone stung, and she rushed out of his office and closed the double doors before several fat teardrops spilled from her eyes and trickled down her cheeks. Now she had done it, she thought bleakly, brushing the tears away with the back of one hand. Ty was the only man she would probably ever love, and now she had made him so angry that he would undoubtedly find it difficult to even be pleasant to her.

Chapter Eleven

Early that evening, after Ty had driven her home from the office, Anne hurriedly changed out of the suit she had worn to work. Immediately after slipping into jeans and a comfortable cotton bouclé sweater, she walked down the hall to Jenny's room. She knocked twice, but no response was forthcoming. She eased open the door to look inside, just to be certain Jenny wasn't merely asleep.

The room was deserted and unusually untidy. Contents were spilling from opened drawers, and several items of clothing, still on hangers, had been tossed onto the bed. As Anne looked around at the mess Jenny had left, suspicion began to drag at her stomach, then became a very intense dread, as she noticed the envelope propped against a perfume atomizer on the vanity table.

Curiously enough, the envelope bore her name, but when Anne tore it open with shaking fingers, then read the contents of the brief note inside, she knew why Jenny hadn't left it for Ty. No doubt, she had been afraid to. The note said that she was going away for the weekend and wouldn't be back until late Sunday night.

Feeling rather ill, Anne simply stared at it for several long moments. After that phone call last night, she could only assume that Kirt had finally beguiled Jenny with his lies. She was such an innocent that she believed he really cared about her, and now it looked as if he had succeeded in persuading her to go away with him.

But where had they gone? Anne wondered frantically. And was it too late to find them before Jenny had to spend a night with Kirt? Having no answers to these questions, she went to Ty, hoping he would know what to do.

When Anne knocked on Ty's bedroom door a few seconds later, he was in the process of changing clothes, too. Clad only in snug-fitting khaki pants, he was pulling the bottom of a rugby-type black knit shirt over his broad tan chest as he opened the door. Obvious surprise at seeing her there flitted across his dark face, then was gone in an instant.

Anne didn't speak. She merely handed him the note, then clenched her hands together before her as he read it. The explosion she had half expected didn't occur, although the implacable hardening of his jaw indicated he was angry. He crushed the note in his hand. His eyes had taken on an ominous glitter as they sought hers.

"It's obvious you're thinking the same thing I am," he said tersely. "Jenny hasn't gone off for the weekend with a girlfriend. If she had, she would have mentioned a name. So she must be with Callen." Uttering an implicit curse, he raked his fingers through his hair. "She's only seventeen, and if he seduces her, I swear I'll have him charged with statutory rape."

Anne put her hand on his arm, an automatic calming

gesture. "Maybe we can do something to avoid that. If we could find them tonight before . . . well, before anything happens, we could just bring Jenny back home. And I've been trying to think where he might have taken her. I believe Jenny would refuse to go to a hotel with him, so maybe he took her to that house he owns near Colonial Beach."

Ty considered her suggestion for a moment, then shook his head. "No, I don't think he'd take her there. He'd probably expect me to go there looking for them. But I do know somewhere else they might have gone. Up to the mountain house."

"But Ellie's there," Anne argued logically. "And Kirt would be risking his life if he tried to seduce Jenny with her in the same house. She impressed me as the kind of lady who would go after him with a cast-iron frying pan for being such a cad."

"She probably would," Ty agreed, smiling grimly at the thought. "The problem is, she isn't at the mountain house right now. She's spending a month with her daughter in Arizona, and Jenny knows that."

"Then they might be there. Hurry, Ty, we have to drive up right away," Anne implored, tugging at his sleeve until she realized he might not want her to go with him. A rose color tinted her cheeks as her hand dropped away from his arm. "I'm sorry. I didn't mean to invite myself along."

"I think you'd better go with me, Anne," he muttered stiffly. "To put it bluntly, Jenny might need you if they are there and we get there too late. I don't imagine Kirt would be a very sensitive first lover for any girl."

Warmth tingled in Anne's cheeks as she agreed. "No, I'm sure he wouldn't be."

"We'll leave as soon as you can get ready then."

"I'm ready now."

"No, not quite. It's unusually chilly tonight," Ty

reminded her. "Get a jacket or something, and I'll meet you downstairs."

The silent, tension-filled drive took over two hours and seemed even longer than that to Anne. Every time she glanced cautiously at Ty, she saw that he was gripping the steering wheel so tightly his knuckles were white. His carved profile, silhouetted in the light from the dash, was menacing. She swallowed with difficulty, and her heart pounded every time she looked at him. She had a feeling Kirt Callen would wish he'd never even spoken to Jenny before this night ended.

As Ty parked the Mercedes in front of the house, Anne suddenly realized that something was missing. "No cars," she remarked. "But I guess they could have parked them in the garage."

"Maybe," Ty said as he thrust open his door with more violence than she had ever seen him display before.

"There are no lights on in the house either," she added a moment later, as they reached the front door. "I hope that doesn't mean . . ."

"That they're already in bed together," Ty finished for her, his tone threatening. "Kirt had better hope it doesn't mean that, too."

As it turned out, entering the house was blessedly anticlimactic. No one was there, and Anne felt a mixture of relief and disappointment. She hadn't wanted to even imagine what Ty was going to do to Kirt if they'd found him here, yet now that they hadn't, they had no hope of finding Jenny tonight.

"Where could she be?" Anne asked urgently, after Ty had checked all the rooms and they were standing once again in the entrance foyer. "Do you have any idea where else Kirt might have taken her?"

"None whatsoever," Ty replied, thrusting his hands deep into his trouser pockets as a frown etched his brow. "*Blast!* We're not going to find her tonight. You know that, don't you?"

Anne nodded, unhappiness darkening her eyes. "Oh, Ty, I feel responsible for this mess. I obviously didn't read Jenny's mood correctly. She seemed so much more content since we got back from St. Croix. I just didn't think she was ready to take a step like this. But I was wrong and I'm so sorry. If I'd known she might do something like this, I would have warned you . . ."

"Hush, Anne," he commanded softly, touching her cheek with the back of his hand. "This isn't your fault. If it is, then it's mine, too, because I didn't think she was capable of this either. But maybe we both simply forgot that people who aren't stupid can act stupidly on occasion. And apparently, this is one of those occasions for Jenny."

"She's just so confused," Anne whispered miserably. Then a sudden hope brightened her face. "Call Mrs. Wilkes, Ty," she urged excitedly. "Maybe Jenny changed her mind and decided to go home. She could be there right now."

He shook his head. "I doubt it. I think that's wishful thinking on your part."

"But it wouldn't hurt to call and be sure. Please do, Ty."

His eyes narrowed and swept over her intently, but at last he nodded. Then he indicated with a gesture that she should precede him into the glass-enclosed living room, so he could make the call from there.

When he reached Mrs. Wilkes, Anne learned nothing from his end of the conversation. After he had asked about Jenny, he listened for awhile, thanked the housekeeper, then replaced the receiver. But as he turned to Anne, he was smiling, though somewhat sheepishly. "I think we have a classic case of over-reaction here," he announced wryly. "Jenny has called Mrs. Wilkes and left a number where she can be reached. Fortunately, I recognize the number—it's Beth MacKay's. I know Beth's parents, so I don't think Jenny is lying about being at their house, because she knows it would be very easy for me to find out if she wasn't there. So it looks as if we jumped the gun a little, doesn't it? Jenny isn't spending the weekend with Kirt."

Anne's relief was so intense that she reached for his hands without thinking. As her chilled skin made contact with the warmth of his, Ty caught her fingers in a gentle grip. "Your hands are freezing. Are you that cold?"

"Well, it was pretty chilly outside, but I'm fine, really."

"I'll get you a brandy," he said, leaving her to go to the bar. A moment later, he returned with a small crystal snifter, which he gave to her.

Taking a sip of the warming brandy, she watched as he went to start a roaring blaze in the stone fireplace. When he had finished, she was happy to go warm herself before the leaping flames.

Leaning one elbow on the mantel, Ty smiled down at her, but as he started to speak, a persistent scratching noise at the front door claimed his attention. "Goldie, no doubt," he said wryly, as he strode from the room.

A few seconds after he had opened the front door, the golden dog trotted into the living room, her tail wagging an enthusiastic welcome as she headed straight for Anne. "Why, I think she remembers me," Anne said, a pleased smile curving her lips as she scratched behind the dog's ears. Dropping onto her knees on the fur rug before the fireplace, she stroked Goldie's silken coat, then glanced up at Ty. "Who takes care of her while Ellie's away?"

"Ellie's oldest grandson comes by every day to feed her." With lithe ease, Ty settled onto the rug beside Anne and patted the dog's sleek head. Then, leaning back on his elbows, he watched the crackling flames lick over and between the logs in the fireplace. "But I'm sure she's missing Ellie. Dogs need to be with people."

And indeed, Goldie seemed grateful to have some human companionship again. Stretching out between Anne and Ty, she rested her soft black nose on his thigh, heaved a sigh of pure contentment, and promptly went to sleep. For a while there was silence in the room, except for the popping and crackling of the logs in the fire. Warmed by the fire and the brandy, Anne sighed contentedly, too, and smiled at Ty, as the soft sound attracted his attention.

For a long moment, his blue gaze drifted over her, then he stood abruptly, reached down for her hands and drew her up to stand before him. "You must be getting hungry. I know I am. We missed dinner, remember," he said tonelessly. "Why don't we go see what we can find in the kitchen? I'm sure Ellie left the refrigerator bare, but there must be some canned goods in the pantry."

With Ty's help, Anne made a delicious little supper, and after they'd eaten, they returned to the living room where the fire was dying down. To Anne's surprise, Ty added a couple more logs, arranging them with a poker until the flames were leaping again. Apparently sensing her watchful gaze, he turned and said nonchalantly, "It's past ten-thirty, so I suggest we spend the night here. There's no point in driving back to Alexandria this late when we're both tired."

She nodded in agreement. Refusing to stay would have made her look foolish. Yet, the irony of the situation wasn't lost on her. They had rushed up here to save Jenny from being seduced, and now Anne found herself alone for the night in an isolated house with the man she loved, the man she knew she might not be able to resist if he attempted to seduce her.

Ty, however, apparently had no such intentions. After spending another hour talking in the living room, they went upstairs and he bid her a cool goodnight.

Though Anne hadn't expected to fall asleep easily, she did, almost the moment her head touched the pillow. Emotionally weary, she slept deeply for awhile. Some hours later, however, she drifted into a state of partial awareness, knowing that she was cold and shivering, yet still too much in the grip of sleep to do anything about it. She had put on one of Jenny's nightgowns, but it didn't seem to be keeping her warm at all. Then she felt a sudden gentle weight settle on the bed, and her eyes flickered open. Seeing the large dark form of a man beside her bed, she gave a soft, startled cry.

"It's all right, Anne. It's only me," Ty quickly assured her, his voice low and melodiously comforting. "I'm putting another blanket over you. The furnace seems to have broken down, and it's freezing in here."

Fully awake now, Anne became immediately aware of the fact that her nose felt like a small iceberg on her face. As she touched it with equally cold fingers, she also noticed that Ty was shivering as he stood by the bed, clad only in a short terry robe. A totally unreasonable compulsion made her hold out her hand to him, and she whispered, "Come to bed, Ty. We can keep each other warm."

"I don't think that's a very wise idea," he muttered, but her persistence was his undoing. As she caught one hand in hers, then drew the covers back invitingly, he could no longer resist. Lowering himself down onto the mattress beside her, he pulled the covers back over both of them.

Anne tensed, yet the delightful warmth of Ty's body close to hers was so enticing, that she soon relaxed again. She made no effort to resist, even when one muscular arm went around her slender waist and Ty unceremoniously turned her over onto her side, then curved his lean, dangerous body around the slightness of hers. When his hand spread open possessively across her abdomen, she did tremble a little, but he ignored that reaction and resolutely drew her tight against him.

"Go back to sleep, Anne," he commanded softly, close to her ear.

At that moment, sleep was the last thing on her mind. As his warm, minty breath stirred tendrils of her hair and tickled the sensitive skin of her neck, desires much more intense than her need to sleep flared deep within. Yet, as she started to turn over to face him, his arm round her waist clamped her firmly against his hardening thighs, forcing her to be aware of his swift, upsurging response to her every movement.

"Be very careful, Anne," he warned huskily. "Unless you want more warmth in this bed than you bargained for, I advise you to stop moving."

"But Ty," she began, shifting nervously against him. "I . . ."

"Just be still," he muttered harshly. "Or you'd better be prepared to accept the consequences, and I don't think you are. Are you?" And when her lack of an answer became an answer in itself, he gave an exasperated sigh and once again told her tersely to go back to sleep.

The lilting call of a bird in the gray light of dawn awakened Anne later. Her eyes fluttered open, widening slightly, as she saw that in her sleep she had turned toward Ty and was now lying in his embrace. There was an evocative heaviness in the arm flung across her breasts, yet she made no move to escape. She didn't want to disturb him. His head rested on her tousled hair on the pillow, and her gaze moved almost hungrily over his lean face. In sleep, he looked younger, despite the dark stubble of a day's growth of beard on his chin, and there was a gentler curving of his firmly carved mouth.

She impulsively feathered her fingers across his cheek. Though her breath caught as he suddenly opened his eyes, she smiled rather shyly. But Ty didn't return the smile. The initial drowsiness of his gaze quickly altered to a hypnotizing, consuming passion, and the fiery blue glint that flared in his eyes impaled the luminous gray of hers. His hand slipped down to cup one breast as he muttered, "Anne, you shouldn't look at me that way."

Her half-frightened gasp was captured by a seeking, possessive kiss that sent her senses spinning. Hardening lips that conveyed little gentleness plundered the softness of hers and opened her mouth to the invading tip of his tongue. Yet, there was tenderness in the large hand that possessed her straining breasts, squeezing and caressing and teasing the sensitive peaks until they hardened beneath the touch of his fingers. Pushing her straps off her shoulders, he pulled her gown down, seeking bare skin. As the rough edge of his thumb rubbed slowly over first one pulsating nipple, then the other, a consuming blaze was ignited in her. Her fingers tangled in his hair. She arched against him, exquisite sensations quickening inside her as his tongue explored the sensitive flesh of her inner cheek.

With his muffled groan, his hand covered one slight hipbone, pressing her back into the softness of the mattress and holding her fast as he rolled over swiftly, pinning her body beneath his. Brushing her hair back from her face, he kissed her again and again, taking her soft trembling lips with a devouring passion she soon realized was beyond his control.

She struggled instinctively, pressing her hands against his broad muscular chest, but such resistance was ineffectual beneath his superior strength. As his teeth closed gently on the soft curve of her lower lip, she twisted beneath him, and at last, managed to drag her mouth from his. "Don't," she gasped. "Ty, please, I can't."

"This time you can't stop me, Anne," he whispered roughly, catching her face between his hands. "I need you too much."

She was truly afraid of him. Fear surged through her veins, mingling with the hot desires aroused by his hard lips taking hers again. Afraid of herself for wanting to surrender, terrified of his uncontrollable passion, she pushed against him again, and a soft sob escaped her as one hard knee parted her thighs. Tears spilled from her eyes, wetting her cheeks, and she couldn't stop them.

"Blast it, don't cry," Ty muttered gruffly after a moment. Then, with a curse uttered beneath his breath, he rolled over and sat up on the edge of the bed, massaging the back of his neck with an oddly shaking hand. As he turned his head, his narrowed gaze swept over her. When he saw that she was still trembling violently, he stood and glared down at her, his expression grim. "I can't take much more of this," he warned tautly, a glint of passion still in his eyes. "You're going to have to decide whether you want me or not, Anne, and you'd better decide soon."

Watching the straight, implacable line of his back as he strode out of the room, Anne raised trembling fingers to her temples. Her gaze sought the window, and she looked out at the blue mist of morning, veiling the rolling mountains, shimmering through the tears that suddenly blurred her vision. Closing her eyes, she turned her face into the pillow and wrapped her arms around her waist. Without Ty in the bed close to her, the chill of the room permeated the covers. She shivered, feeling as if she would never be warm again. If only he could understand that making a decision wasn't as simple for her as it might have been. If she had even a small hope that he might begin to love her someday, she would surrender to him happily. But knowing about his involvement with Millicent Beaumont changed everything.

Chapter Twelve

The following Tuesday evening there was a knock on Ty's front door just as Anne started down the stairs. Before she could make a move to answer it, however, Ty left the study and went to the door himself. Anne halted halfway down the stairs, then smiled when she recognized Mike's voice. Hoping he had come to see Jenny, she descended one more step, but her smile faded abruptly when Ty spoke.

"Sorry, Mike, but Anne's busy," he announced flatly. "She can't see you now. Call her later or see her at the office tomorrow. Goodnight."

"Wait, Ty," Anne called, running lightly down the remaining steps and across the hall. Intending to tell him Mike was probably there to see Jenny, she touched his arm imploringly. "Let him in, please. He's . . ."

"No," he muttered, his jaw clenched. Then to her astonishment, and despite Mike's nearly comical befuddlement, he closed the door firmly in the young man's face.

Anne stared incredulously at the thunderous expression that darkened Ty's features. "I warned you, Anne," he said too quietly. "You won't go out with Mike while I'm paying you to be here."

All Anne's pent-up resentment and pain erupted. Angry color blazed in her cheeks as she clenched her hands into fists at her sides. He cared nothing about her, yet he controlled her entire existence. She could tolerate his attitude no longer. "Then I think it's time I left your house," she said bitingly. "You can't tell me whom I can or can't go out with. I won't have it. I'm moving back to my own apartment, where I can run my own life. I'm plenty tired of your running it for me."

"You're not leaving," he informed her with infuriating calm, though his blue eyes glittered ominously. "Jenny still needs you."

"Since you're so interested in Jenny's welfare, let me tell you something. She's up in her room right now, crying. That's what I was coming to tell you," Anne declared tautly. "I think I know now why she's been acting so foolishly. She just told me she had an argument with your father the day he died. She wanted to spend the summer in Europe with a friend, but he refused to let her go, since she was only sixteen. So she told him that he was a terrible father. Then he was killed before she could apologize to him. She feels horribly guilty."

"She told you that?" Ty exclaimed. "You mean that's what's been bothering her all this time?"

"I told her she shouldn't feel so guilty," Anne murmured, her anger dissolving to mere weariness of the spirit. "I tried to explain that all parents know children say things they don't really mean. But I couldn't convince her."

"I wish she'd told me all this long ago," Ty muttered, his voice strained. "I talked to Dad after she did that day, and he was laughing about the argument they'd had. Goodness, she was only sixteen. Of course, he wasn't upset when she called him a terrible father! He knew she didn't mean it."

As Ty raked his fingers through his hair, Anne longed to touch him comfortingly. Yet, knowing she had no right to do so, she said instead, "Go tell her, Ty. She'll be so relieved to know your father wasn't angry with her that day. I think it'll make all the difference in her attitude."

"Yes," he murmured absently, removing his loosened tie completely. "Yes, I'll go up and tell her now."

As he started to walk away, Anne took one step after him, an oppressive heaviness squeezing her chest. "She will be all right now, Ty, I'm sure of it," she called softly after him. "You know, she told me that phone call the other night was from Mike Bennett, not Kirt. She hasn't seen him since we got back from St. Croix." When he stopped at the foot of the stairs to look back at her, she tried to force a semblance of a smile. "So when she knows the truth about your father, you won't need me here any longer after all. Please, let me move back to my apartment."

"No, Anne. Don't start packing yet," he replied tonelessly. "Jenny's been through a traumatic year and she may need you here to talk to for quite some time."

"But Ty! I . . ."

"You're staying," he interrupted bluntly, stony blue eyes raking over her. "Resign yourself to it. Besides, Sue needs the extra money I pay you, doesn't she?"

Anne winced, appalled he'd so callously remind her of her financial problems. Squaring her shoulders, she met his eyes directly. "Don't worry about Sue. I'll take care of her money needs . . . somehow."

"Not by moonlighting as a waitress again. Or by taking any other kind of second job," he countered, his expression hard, unyielding. "Don't try that if you want to keep your job as my secretary."

"Are you threatening to fire me again?" she exclaimed, her voice choked with a sudden knot of unshed tears. "If you are, I'll . . ."

"You'll what? What can you do?" he countered mockingly. "You can't help Sue at all if you don't have your job, so it looks as if you'll have to stay here as long as I want you to."

"You really are ruthless, aren't you?" she whispered, her face paling. "I don't understand . . . why you're doing this to me."

"We'll talk about that later. Right now, I want to make Jenny understand she's had no reason to feel guilty," Ty replied blandly, lifting one foot onto the first stair. Then he paused, his enigmatic gaze drifting lazily over Anne once more. "Oh, and by the way, we'll be driving to Charlottesville on business Thursday evening. And we'll be staying overnight."

Too stunned by his cruelty, Anne couldn't even nod in acknowledgement. Her eyes overflowed with tears as he took the stairs, two at a time, on his way up to comfort Jenny. So, he thought it was back to business as usual. Wounded deeply by his cool aloofness, Anne pressed her fingers to her lips. It could never be business as usual for her again, especially if she had to remain in his house, so close to him, yet worlds apart.

Darkness was falling around the Mercedes Thursday evening when Anne suddenly realized that Ty seemed to be taking a strange route to Charlottesville. She glanced curiously at him out of the corner of her eye, but said nothing, supposing he knew what he was doing. A half hour later, however, when he turned the Mercedes onto the winding parkway that they usually traveled to reach his mountain house, she felt compelled to say something. "Isn't this sort of a roundabout way to get to Charlottesville?" she asked somewhat hesitantly. "I've never gone there this way before."

"There's been a change of plan," he answered flatly, expertly manuevering the Mercedes around the sharp curves with one lean hand on the steering wheel. "We aren't going to Charlottesville. We're going up to the house."

"Oh, I see," Anne murmured, though she really didn't. "I'm surprised Mrs. Morehead's willing to come up here to discuss her investments. I thought she hated to leave Charlottesville and that's why we were going to see her."

Taking his eyes from the road for a brief instant, Ty gave her a bland look. "As I said, there's been a change of plan."

Since he was obviously disinclined to offer any further explanation, Anne didn't press him for one. Instead, she gazed out her window at the dark bowl of the Shenandoah Valley, where tiny lights in tiny houses glowed warm and cozy in the night.

Ty said nothing, even after he had parked the car in front of the mountain house. As he took their suitcases from the back seat and Goldie bounded ecstatically around his feet, a sudden realization made Anne speak up. "Oh dear," she sighed. "What are we going to feed Mrs. Morehead while she's here? Remember, Ellie left the refrigerator bare."

"I brought some groceries," he answered flatly, indicating she should precede him up the veranda steps. "They're in the trunk. I'll come get them after I get this luggage inside."

A minute or so later, while he went back for the

supplies, Anne carried her suitcase upstairs and set about unpacking her things. She took a sharp breath as Ty suddenly appeared in the doorway, dark and lean and overwhelmingly masculine in a dove gray suit.

As she gave him a rather shy smile, he unbuttoned his vest and removed his wine-colored tie. "You might as well not unpack in here," he announced abruptly. "I'll take your bag into my room because you'll be sleeping there tonight."

The low, lazy cadence of his voice seemed almost provocative. Anne's heart began a frantic beat, but she chided herself for simply having an over-active imagination. Lifting her delicately arched brows questioningly, she looked at him. "I don't understand exactly what you mean. If you're going to give your room to someone, shouldn't it be to Mrs. Morehead?"

"Mrs. Morehead isn't coming, Anne." Smiling at her baffled expression, he removed his jacket as he added, "We weren't ever going to Charlottesville to see her either. I only told you that so I could bring you up here."

Anne's pulses hammered and as her legs went weak, she reached out to grasp the bedpost for support. "What do you mean?" she squeaked. "Why did you . . ."

"We have a great deal to talk about, and I decided we need complete privacy," he said calmly, though a hint of a smile tugged at the corners of his mouth. "But we can discuss everything later. Now, I'm going down to put the eggs and milk into the refrigerator."

"Don't you dare leave!" Anne called impulsively as he started to turn away from the door. But as he turned back to face her, she modified her command. "I mean, you can't just walk away after . . . after telling me we're going to be alone here and that I'll . . . be sleeping in your bed. You have to explain."

"Oh, I intend to," he said softly, coming to her, taking both her hands. "And the first thing we're going to discuss is your plan to move back to your apartment."

"I plan to move back soon," she muttered, disappointment causing sharp pain to radiate through her chest. "I thought I could do it Monday evening, after work."

Darkening blue eyes searched her face. "Is that really what you want to do, Anne?" he whispered, and when she was unable to answer him, he shook his head. "No, I don't think you want to move out of my house. So, you'll stay."

"How can I? Jenny won't even be there," Anne whispered back weakly, too aware of his nearness. "I can't just live with you, Ty, for no good reason."

"I thought maybe just being with me would be a good enough reason. Wouldn't it be?"

Anne's wide gray eyes searched his face for some indication that he was teasing, but when she saw that he seemed perfectly serious, she asked stiffly, "Are you asking me to become your mistress?"

A soft laugh came from deep in his throat. "Something like that, yes. Now give me an answer. Will you live with me?"

"No!" she gasped. "I couldn't do that!"

"But why couldn't you?" he murmured coaxingly, drawing her closer and lowering his dark head. Firm lips brushed her cheeks. "I think you care about me, Anne, and I know you want me. You're a passionate young woman, and I've known that since the first time I kissed you. So why shouldn't we share something beautiful together?"

As his lean hands spanned her waist and his lips trailed nearer her mouth, she could feel her resolve weakening. It took all the self-control she could muster to shore it up again. But she did. She shook her head emphatically, resentment and hurt darkening her gaze. "I have some pride, Ty, even if I am merely a secretary," she muttered, her voice strained. "I won't . . . I couldn't just live with you for awhile. And I don't see how you can even ask me to. I'm sure Millicent Beaumont wouldn't approve of such an arrangement."

He tensed. Lifting his head, he stared down at her upturned face, the blue light that flared in his eyes piercing hers. "What the devil are you talking about? What does Millicent have to do with you and me?"

"Don't play games with me, Ty, please," Anne exclaimed softly, unable to drag her pain-darkened gaze from his. "I know about you and Millicent. Jenny told me you were planning to marry her once, and now that she's left her husband, you and she . . ." Her words broke off as he pulled her violently against him. Her chin quivered. "Why are you doing this to me? Let me go, please, Ty."

"No, I'm not letting you go. Ever," he answered relentlessly, capturing her chin in one hand. Yet, there was something akin to tender indulgence in the gaze that drifted slowly over her face. He shook his head incredulously. "Anne, if Millicent is the reason you suddenly went all cold on me, then we've wasted the past few weeks for nothing. Because I am not involved romantically with Millicent Beaumont, and I haven't been for years."

"You can't expect me to believe that!" Anne exclaimed, trying to free herself from his iron-hard grip, but failing completely. "If you're not involved with her, then why have you been spending every waking minute with her lately? Why? Answer me that!"

"Don't exaggerate, Anne," he chided gently, wrapping his arms firmly around her slenderness. "I haven't been spending every waking minute with Millicent and you know it. I *have* been trying to help her through a difficult time. Her husband's pressing for a reconciliation, and she really wants to go back to him, but her family's keeping her in a state of constant confusion. They disapprove of Luke Beaumont and, in fact, never wanted her to marry him. So they're pressuring her to divorce him now. She just needed someone to talk to, and she chose me."

"I still don't believe you," Anne muttered, though she had to fight back the hope that was rising in her. "If she loves him, why doesn't she just tell her family to stay out of her business and go back to him, where she belongs? I don't believe she needs your shoulder to cry on just because her family gives her a difficult time."

"Anne, love," he whispered earnestly, smiling as her lips parted in response to the enticing endearment. "Not everyone is as strong-willed as you are. Millicent certainly isn't. She's been too pampered all her life. She can hardly decide which dress to buy without someone's advice. And now, with Luke begging her to come back to him and her family constantly warning her she shouldn't, she's on the verge of a nervous breakdown. She was actually threatening to do something desperate for awhile. I couldn't turn my back on her when she called me for help, could I?"

Hope bloomed in Anne, making her giddy. Clutching his crisp white shirtfront, she searched his dark beloved face as she breathed, "Ty, is that the truth? Is it really?"

"It is, really," he murmured, drawing her up on tiptoe, his hands molding her hips and pressing her against the hard strength of his thighs. Flames of desire flickered in his eyes. "Anne, how could you think I was involved with Millicent, when it was obvious I could hardly keep my hands off you? Since the day you became my secretary, there's been no other woman in my life. I only want you. You're intelligent and caring and lovely to look at and to touch. And I love you."

"You might have told me that and saved me a lot of miserable moments," she complained half-heartedly, tears of happiness filling her eyes. "Oh Ty, I love you so much and I've needed to know you loved me. I wish you'd told me how you felt weeks ago."

"I think I did," he said wryly, brushing the edge of his thumb across the soft curve of her lips. "Why else do you think I made you quit working at the restaurant and come live with me? I used Jenny as my excuse, but, Anne, didn't you know I really made you do it because I couldn't stand to watch you working so hard to keep Sue in school? You were beginning to look so tired and very fragile, at least to me. I wanted to look after you. I still do, and I want you to look after me, if you want to. Jenny told me that Mike was at the house to see her the other night, so I'm not worried about him. But . . . what about the other man, the one you worked for, the one who hurt you. Can you forget him?"

"Oh Ty, I was only infatuated with him. I was eighteen, so I was hurt and embarrassed when I realized he wasn't serious about me. But I never loved him, and he *is* forgotten. You're the only man I could never forget. I love you and, yes, I do want to look after you for the rest of our lives."

"Then you're going to have to marry me, Anne. You know that, don't you?"

Too overwhelmed with happiness to answer in words, Anne stretched up on tiptoe, arching against him. As his mouth covered hers gently at first, then with deepening rousing demand, that central throbbing ache he always created in her flared to life again. Yet, this time was different. She could surrender completely to the desire he evoked and to him. He loved her, and tonight she would belong to him. Trembling fingers unbuttoned his shirt. Her hands brushed lovingly across his chest, her fingernails catching in the fine dark hair. "I love you so much, Ty," she whispered, pressing her lips against his firm bronze skin, then lifting her mouth to his again.

His marauding kiss drained all the strength from her limbs, and she was warmly acquiescent as he unzipped her dress to push it off her shoulders. It slipped down to the floor around her feet and was soon followed by her slip. And though her breath caught as he removed the fragile wisps of lace that were the remaining barriers between them, she felt delightfully vulnerable and desired when he held her from him and allowed his gaze to wander slowly over every satin-textured inch of her body.

Her gray eyes were drowsy with passion, and as he cupped her firm throbbing breasts in strong gentle hands, her lips parted with a swiftly indrawn breath of anticipation. Covering his hands with hers, she glanced at the bed behind her. "Love me, Ty," she whispered invitingly. "Love me, now."

"Yes, I'm going to but not in here," he murmured huskily. With lithe ease, as if she weighed nothing at all, he swept her up in his arms and strode across the hall to his own room. "I've wanted you in my bed for so long, Anne, and that's where I'm going to make love to you."

By then, she didn't much care where he made love to her, just as long as he did. Lying on his bed, she watched with half-closed eyes as he swiftly undressed, then she lifted her arms to him. His devouring gaze swept over the entrancing curves of her slender body, then he was beside her on the bed, finding her mouth, parting her soft lips with fierce demanding power until she was weak with longing for him. His hands roamed over her, caressing her breasts, stroking her abdomen and the gentle outcurving of her hips. As her lips clung hungrily to his and she wrapped her arms tightly around his waist, he lowered his weight gently onto her slight body.

"I love you, Anne," he whispered roughly. But his hand was gentle as he caressed her thighs, coaxing them apart with the exquisite brushing touch of his thumb. And as she quivered beneath him, his other hand under her hips arched her upward to receive him.

His lips captured her first soft gasp and, then, the shuddering sigh of delight as their bodies merged perfectly. "Anne, *love,*" he murmured triumphantly as she pressed closer, seeking all the hard warmth of his body. Whispering endearments in her ear, nibbling the tender lobe with his teeth, he began to move slowly, rousingly against her until she started to move with him, warmly feminine and delightfully pliant and completely his.

Her desire heightened his, and he swept her along in a turmoil of dizzying, piercing passion that culminated in waves of exquisite pleasure rippling deep within her. She was lost in sensations she had never really known existed, and she caught her breath as fulfillment radiated warmth throughout her body. She was so sensitized to his touch that she trembled violently as his hard, warm lips took possession of the throbbing peak of one breast, but she arched against him, pressing him down to her, finding even more delight in giving fulfillment to his intolerable need, as he took her with tender, yet demanding, strength.

Much later, Anne smiled as Ty brushed his lips across her bare shoulder. When he pulled her over onto her side and lay gazing at her lovingly, she cupped his dark face in her hands. "I love you, Ty," she whispered. "So very much."

"You'd better," he whispered back teasingly, "since

we're going to see what we can do about getting married tomorrow." After stroking her hair back from one cheek, he lightly tapped the tip of her small nose. "And after you become Mrs. Manning, Miss Fairchild, I do hope you're going to let me help you pay Sue's college expenses."

"I might," she answered pertly. "But only if you let me keep my job as your secretary."

Ty's expression sobered. "I thought you might want to go to college with Sue and Jenny. If that's what would make you happy, you know I wouldn't object."

In that moment, her love for him was dizzying in its intensity. "You're a wonderful man," she whispered, stroking his face adoringly, then giving him a coy smile. "But I don't think I want to go to college now. Maybe someday, but not for a long time. I'm not about to let some other secretary take my place and fall in love with you. I couldn't bear to lose you."

"You never will," he promised. "So if you do want to enroll in college . . ."

"I'd rather spend every day with you," she interrupted, pressing one silencing finger against his lips. "And, after all, you said once that I was the best secretary you'd ever had."

"And the sexiest, by far," he agreed, smiling wickedly. "But you'd better remember that sofa in my office. If you're my secretary, we might not get a great deal of work done."

"Umm, that sounds like a terrific fringe benefit," she quipped, laughing softly until his lips descended on hers and brought a sudden lovely silence to the room.